Planning & Growing a Business Venture

VENTURE PLANNING

WORKBOOK

2004 EDITION

Ewing Marion
KAUFFMAN
Foundation

FAST TRAC ®

TAKE CHARGE OF YOUR BUSINESS ®

A program of the Kauffman Foundation of Kansas City

TAKE CHARGE OF YOUR BUSINESS®

Visit our Web sites at:
www.fasttrac.org
www.kauffman.org

Acknowledgments

Original FastTrac Program Authors

Richard H. Buskirk, Ph.D.
R. Mack Davis
Courtney Price, Ph.D.

Editorial Team

Ewing Marion Kauffman Foundation
Judith Cone
Stefanie Weaver
Kathryn Nadlman, Project Consultant
Jodie Trana, Advant•Edge Business Services
David J. André, Attorney & Counselor at Law
Nancy Allbee, Editorial Production Services
Leslee Anne Terpay, Terpay Knowledge Resources
J. Diane Awbrey, Ph.D.
Andrea F. Sellers, Stinson Mag & Fizzel PC

Ewing Marion Kauffman

The late entrepreneur and philanthropist Ewing Kauffman established the Ewing Marion Kauffman Foundation as the first foundation to focus on entrepreneurship as one of its primary areas of interest.

There is more to Ewing Kauffman's beneficence than his fortune. He had an instinct for the future. He understood how to bring organizations to life to be productive and vital. Above all, he had a zest for life and a social awareness that was grounded in his belief in people. The Kauffman Foundation of Kansas City develops and advances innovative ideas that set the groundwork for institutional change, advance entrepreneurship in America, and improve the academic achievement of children and youth.

From modest beginnings, Kauffman grew Marion Laboratories into a billion dollar pharmaceutical giant and established the Kansas City Royals, bringing major league baseball back to Kansas City. With his business succeeding beyond his wildest dreams, Kauffman turned his vigor, intellect, and wealth to a new style of philanthropy. He lost patience with charity work that never seemed to attack the core problem it sought to remedy. He wanted to dig deep and get at the roots of issues rather than talk about addressing the symptoms. Undaunted by the size of the challenge or the lack of resources, Kauffman encouraged his staff to become immersed in research, consult with the best minds, and devise bold approaches to address complex social problems. He told friends he was having more fun giving money away than he had earning it. He told associates he expected his foundation to be exemplary.

An epitome of American entrepreneurship, Kauffman saw business enterprise as one of the most effective ways to unleash human potential and stir the economy to life. He viewed entrepreneurship as the most powerful strategy to help individuals gain economic independence and serve as a catalyst for creating jobs and wealth in society. Today the Kauffman Foundation is devoted to advancing entrepreneurship as one of the fundamental aspects of life in the United States. Focusing on research, education, technical assistance, and policy, we work to increase the number and success rate of individuals engaged in the process of starting or growing their own business or idea. We work with partners to design programs based on the proven principles, techniques, and leadership tactics that make starting and growing a business a more common choice for Americans of all walks of life.

The Kauffman Foundation's FastTrac programs are part of a wide range of resources developed in collaboration with hundreds of successful entrepreneurs who have shared their knowledge, insights, and stories so that others might learn from them. We hope that all entrepreneurs will find them useful as they work to write their own entrepreneurial success stories.

For more information on FastTrac, the nation's leading, award-winning business training program for entrepreneurs, go to www.fasttrac.org or call (800) 669-1740. To order FastTrac materials, including *Planning and Growing a Business Venture: Venture Planning Field Guide, Venture Planning Workbook*, and *The Business Mentor* CD-ROM, call the FastTrac fulfillment center at (877) 450-9800. For more information about the Kauffman Foundation and entrepreneurship, go www.kauffman.org, or call (800) 489-4900.

Table of Contents

The Importance of Planning

The *Venture Planning Workbook* was created to assist the student in developing the planning skills necessary for the start-up through growth stages of a business. The saying that people read better than they hear has been proven time and again. Entrepreneurs frequently do not understand why they should plan or how they should prepare the planning documents essential to operating a successful business. Entrepreneurs tend to not write their plans down; instead, they carry the plans in their heads. This workbook will make it easier for entrepreneurs to better express themselves on paper and prepare professional planning documents for managing their businesses, as well as for investors to evaluate.

One of the most frequently asked questions is, "Are entrepreneurs born or made?" Some aspects of entrepreneurship, such as possessing certain entrepreneurial characteristics, may be inherent in the individual. However, many aspects are definitely learned behaviors. Planning, one of the key success factors of entrepreneurship, is definitely a learned skill.

One of the biggest problems for students is trying to write feasibility and business plans when they don't know what questions or issues need to be addressed. For this reason, the *Venture Planning Workbook* has been designed to feature a question-and-answer format in each section where it is appropriate. Students should answer the questions as they move through the workbook. After finishing each module, they will have essentially developed a feasibility or business plan. All that remains is to rewrite the answers in a paragraph format.

Students have an electronic tool, *The Business Mentor*™ CD-ROM, to use in their business-planning process. The CD-ROM consists of computer templates, which give students a jump start in producing feasibility or business plans. The templates save students time by assisting with formatting, organizing, and presenting business decisions and information. (Microsoft® Excel is needed to use the financial spreadsheets.)

These electronic templates allow students to record decisions as they progress through the training modules. Business plan topics are preformatted so information can be entered directly. Built-in helpful hints provide students additional business-planning assistance.

Business ventures are never stagnant. They are either expanding or declining as a result of sales volume or other factors affecting the business. Therefore, constant monitoring, reviewing, and adjusting through the planning process outlined in this workbook can help ensure the business's continued success.

Do not fall into the trap of over-planning. Once the necessary plans have been completed, successful entrepreneurs can then spend their effort executing the plans.

Remember that good advice is available from many different sources in the infrastructure, including accountants, lawyers, bankers, and consultants. Heed their advice, but it is strongly recommended not to have someone else write your plan. If you feel that your writing skills are weak and would negatively affect the professionalism of the plan, answer all the questions in the book that pertain to your business and then have someone else, such as an editor, finalize your planning documents.

Entrepreneurs' plans are their calling cards to the business world. Learn to prepare them professionally, and you will experience many good returns.

How to Use this Workbook

The *Venture Planning Workbook* answers the planning problems of starting, running, and growing ventures. It benefits all those involved in the entrepreneurial world:

- The entrepreneur who has an idea
- The entrepreneur or investor who needs to evaluate a business concept
- The entrepreneur who has a solid concept but wants to determine if it is feasible
- The entrepreneur who needs a professional feasibility or business plan for potential investors, bankers, and support groups
- The entrepreneur who has an existing business but needs a plan to make the business grow
- The accountant, lawyer, or consultant who helps the entrepreneur plan for a new or existing business
- Bankers who evaluate businesses for possible loans in the start-up and growth stages
- Investment bankers who help the entrepreneur write feasibility or business plans to facilitate preparation of private placements and a prospectus for going public
- Venture capitalists who want to invest in the entrepreneur's business

The *Venture Planning Workbook* includes the following:

Introduction helps students understand why it is important to learn the planning process needed to start and manage new ventures.

Feasibility plan includes a hard copy of the questions (and hints) that need to be to answered for a feasibility plan. Many students requested the hard copy to support the CD-ROM.

Business plan sections to be completed as homework assist the student in developing a business plan.

Sample feasibility or business plans can be found electronically on *The Business Mentor* CD-ROM.

The *Venture Planning Workbook* approach to teaching the student how to write feasibility or business plans is like learning how to paint by numbers. Remember how pictures can be painted by using numbers with instructions to paint all the 2s blue and all the 3s red? By the time a person used all the colors required by the painting, there was a picture. The painter may not have added any creativity, but he or she did learn how to apply paint to the canvas. Once the person learned the process of painting, he or she could then apply creativity to future paintings.

The process of learning how to paint is analogous to the process of writing a feasibility or business plan. The *Venture Planning Workbook* teaches students how to create and write plans using the paint-by-numbers approach. A series of introspective questions is provided for students to address and answer when writing feasibility or business plans. Once they understand the questions asked and gather the necessary information to answer those questions, the students have learned the process—a process that can be used over and over again for writing feasibility and business plans.

Students who use this workbook and learn the skill of writing a good plan will understand the planning process, a skill that will help them in the corporate world as well as in the entre-preneurial world.

Learning Objectives

Students using the *Venture Planning Workbook* will

- Understand the process for analyzing the feasibility of business concepts.
- Demonstrate the process in writing a feasibility or business plan.
- Identify critical steps to gather information needed to decide if a new venture should be started.

What's the Difference?

Feasibility Plan	Business Plan
Executive Summary	Executive Summary
	Management and Organization Plan
Product/Service	Product/Service Plan
The Market • Industry Profile • Customer Profile • Customer Benefits • Target Markets • Market Penetration	**Marketing Plan** • Industry Profile • Customer Profile • Customer Benefits • Target Markets • Market Penetration • Pricing Profile • Competition Profile • Advertising and Labeling • Service and Warranties • Trade Shows • Future Markets
	Financial Plan • Budgets/Assumptions • Cash Flow Projections • Projected Income Statements • Pro Forma Balance Sheet • Financial Analysis Ratios
Price and Profitability • Pricing • Projected Profit and Loss Statements • Estimated Start-Up Costs	
	Operating and Control Systems Plan
	Growth Plan
	Appendix

The Feasibility Plan

Every budding entrepreneur should carefully write a feasibility plan. This plan should be written before investing any money into a new venture. The purpose is to determine whether an idea for starting a new business could turn into a profitable business venture. Usually, the opposite is true.

The entrepreneur gets all wrapped up in the excitement of a new-venture idea without thoughtful consideration, research, and evaluation of its potential and pitfalls. Entering a venture without analyzing its feasibility can be an expensive shortcut. Later, the entrepreneur realizes that the idea was sound, but perhaps the market was saturated. Maybe the profit margin was too narrow. Maybe the management team was not in place. Or perhaps there was not enough capital. There could be many reasons the venture failed.

If entrepreneurs researched new-venture ideas and wrote feasibility plans before starting, many failed businesses would never have been started in the first place. Lack of planning and research is one of the basic reasons so many new businesses fail during the first, tenuous years of operation. Most statistics show that many new start-ups fail during the first year. This failure rate could be significantly reduced if properly structured research and planning were conducted in the beginning, preventing starting up ill-conceived businesses.

Deciding whether to start a new venture takes time for researching the market, making financial forecasts, and writing a sound feasibility plan. Entrepreneurs are reluctant to conduct all of these tasks; they are doers who want to take their ideas to the marketplace quickly. They know that the window of opportunity will probably be open only for a short period of time. Consequently, they avoid taking the necessary time to research and strategically plan their ventures, identifying problem areas and formulating plans to prevent potential roadblocks. If they take the time to plan, they can develop solutions before encountering problems. Shrewd entrepreneurs understand the importance of writing feasibility plans. The plans indicate whether ventures are likely to succeed.

While writing the plan, you can identify which areas pose the greatest threats and develop alternative solutions if a problem should occur. If the feasibility plan demonstrates that the venture idea has potential, the next step is to write a business plan.

Many entrepreneurs think that if they have a great business opportunity that matches their experience and expertise, then the venture will be successful. In reality, finding a business to start is only 10 percent of the work needed before opening up for business. The next step is writing a feasibility analysis to find out if the business could be profitable.

Feasibility plans explore whether venture ideas have the potential to succeed. Writing a feasibility plan forces you to consider every facet of a business opportunity and write the results on paper. Then you and others can objectively evaluate its potential. Every venture has both risks and opportunities. What are the risks compared to the opportunities? What are the potential problems? Could the potential problems be either eliminated or minimized? Developing a feasibility plan addresses these questions. It allows for trial-and-error testing before any dollars are spent.

Sections of a Feasibility Plan

The following outline for a feasibility plan indicates the scope of information that should be researched and included in the plan:

- Cover page
- Table of contents
- Executive summary
- Product/service
- Market analysis
- Price and profitability
- Plan for further action

Most of these sections can be used in the business plan if the concept is shown to be feasible. Each section of this feasibility plan is discussed and outlined, including section titles, checklist questions to answer, and hints for each question.

Cover Page

The cover page includes the name of the business as well as a contact name, address, and phone number and should also include a fax number and e-mail address if available. If a logo has already been designed, display it on the cover page.

A picture or drawing of the product may also be appropriate on the cover or inside the feasibility plan. Art work can be effective when it is relevant to the business concept. The same motif can be used sparingly throughout the plan for visual impact. If you are unsure whether the art work is suitable, seek feedback from experienced advisers. Remember, the goal is to create a professional looking plan. Do not confuse or detract the reader from understanding the purpose of the feasibility plan.

If you are concerned about readers revealing the plan's contents or ideas to other persons and will have more than one plan out for review, place a tracking number on the cover page. To discourage recipients from copying or distributing the plan to others include a statement such as: "The contents of this plan are proprietary and confidential. It is not to be copied or duplicated in any way." You should also consider having the recipient sign a nondisclosure agreement in which the reader agrees to refrain from sharing this information with others. By disclosing information without a signed nondisclosure agreement, you may lose your ability to protect the information through trade secrets, patents, or other types of protection.

Table of Contents

This page includes the sections of the feasibility plan with accompanying page numbers. Many readers do not examine feasibility plans sequentially and rely on the table of contents to direct them to the sections most important to them.

An appendix is optional in a feasibility plan. Use an appendix if there is additional relevant information that cannot be adequately cited within the body of the feasibility plan. If an appendix is used, list "Appendix" as the last item of the table of contents. Include a title page labeled "Appendix" before this section of the plan. Follow the title page with a separate table of contents page listing the exhibits in the appendix. For example, the table of contents of the appendix would read:

Exhibit A	Site analysis
Exhibit A-1	Site map
Exhibit A-2	Demographic data
Exhibit B	Survey results

Business Name

FEASIBILITY PLAN

Feasibility plan prepared by

Entrepreneur's name

Entrepreneur's title

Company address

City, state and zip code

Best numbers to be reached

Date prepared

Month year

Table of Contents

Executive Summary

The executive summary is the first section in the completed feasibility plan. Since the executive summary is intended to be a brief overview of the entire plan, it should be written last. It should be no more than one or two pages in length.

Before writing the executive summary, identify the intended audience of the plan. To whom will the feasibility plan be presented and for what purpose? If a plan has more than one audience, write a different executive summary to highlight specific areas of interest.

Write the executive summary in narrative form using impersonal language. Use your name when referring to yourself in the feasibility plan instead of using "I." Avoid long sentences and phrases.

The executive summary tells your reader what you propose to do, how you intend to do it, what it will cost, and the potential rewards. In many cases, the executive summary is the only section of the plan that an evaluator will read. If the executive summary does not clearly and concisely convey the business concept and its uniqueness, most lenders or investors will not read any further.

Formatting the Executive Summary with section titles

Venture description
  Insert answer to question 1
Product/service
  Insert answer to question 2
Market
  Insert answer to question 3
Start-up costs
  Insert answer to question 4
Price & profitability
  Insert answer to question 5

Executive summary questions

Venture description

1. What business is your venture in? What is the current stage of development for the venture?

In paragraph one of the executive summary, describe the type of business your venture is in. Indicate whether your business is a retail, wholesale, manufacturing, or service business. Identify the current stage of development for the venture (concept stage, start-up, initial operations, expansion, etc.).

Product/service

2. What is unique about the product/service, and what proprietary rights does the business have?

In paragraph two of the executive summary, describe your product/service by emphasizing what is unique. Define your product/service in terms of the problem it will solve or the need it will meet. Promote any proprietary rights the business might have (trademarks, service marks, patents, copyrights, trade secrets, licenses, royalties, distribution rights, and franchise agreements).

Market

3. What is the market like in terms of the industry, the target market, customer needs, product/service benefits, and market-penetration plan?

In paragraph three of the executive summary, describe the market for your product/service in terms of the industry, the target market, customer needs, product benefits, and market penetration plan. Provide the reader with an overview of the market section.

Start-up costs

4. How much money does the venture need for start-up costs?

In paragraph four of the executive summary, identify how much money the venture will need to get started and how this money will be spent.

Pricing & profitability

5. What kind of financing will the company need? How will the funds be repaid? What is the expected profitability of the venture?

In paragraph five of the executive summary, identify the amount of financing needed and potential sources of funds. Detail how the future profits of the company will provide adequate profit, support operations, and payback funding sources.

6. Closing paragraph.

In the closing paragraph, thank the readers and invite them to read further. Remind the readers to feel free to contact you if they have any questions. State that you look forward to meeting with them after they have had the chance to review the feasibility plan.

Product/Service

Many nice-sounding concepts dealing with large markets fail for lack of a sound working product or service. Many business concepts just do not work! Dreaming is at its peak! The technology is not there, or if it is, it is not feasible technology or might cost too much. For example, solar energy was very fascinating as a new technology. Although the concept was great, it was not practical. First, the scientists had to develop small storage facilities that did not consume a large amount of space, as well as develop capabilities for giving the customer a quick payback with cheaper energy alternatives.

Often the proposed product or service has been previously tried and found lacking. Or perhaps the product/service is owned by other parties. Before going any further in a new venture, the entrepreneur must determine if the concept has a working and tested product/service, is owned or licensed by him or her, and is feasible.

One of the most important questions in this section of the feasibility plan is the first one: "What purpose and unique features distinguish your product/service?" The more unique features of a product or service, the better chance the business concept has of being successful.

A good example of this concept is how Callaway Golf Company developed The Big Bertha® golf club. The club was so different from other golf clubs that many golfers were tempted to try it to discover if something this unique would work and improve their golf games and lower their scores. Since the big heads did make the golf ball easier to hit, sales escalated and they were an immediate success.

Formatting the Product/Service section with section titles

Purpose of the product/service
Insert answer to question 1

Stage of development
Insert answer to question 2

Product/service limitations
Insert answer to question 3

Proprietary rights
Insert answer to question 4

Governmental approvals
Insert answer to question 5

Product liability
Insert answer to question 6

Related products/services and spin-offs
Insert answer to question 7

Production
Insert answer to question 8

Product/service questions

Purpose of the product/service

1. What purpose and unique features distinguish your product/service?

Describe the purpose of the product/service in terms of the problem it will solve. List the unique features of the product/service. Use meaningful adjectives that are to the point and easy to understand (avoid adjectives such as "the best" and "the greatest"). Consider how cost, design, quality, capabilities, and the like meet the needs of your customers. Include photographs or sketches as deemed necessary.

Stage of development

2. What is the stage of development of the product/service?

Identify the current stage of development of your venture (idea stage, model stage, working prototype, small production runs, full manufacturing/production, decline or other). Provide the projected dates or estimated time frames for achieving the other stages of development.

Product/service limitations

3.   What are the limitations of your product/service?

Provide an objective evaluation of the limitations of the product/service. Be specific. Examples include perishability, limited shelf life, installation, legal restrictions, and the like. (Bakery goods, medicines, software, and dairy products are examples of products that have limited shelf lives.)

Proprietary rights

4.   What proprietary rights exist for your product/service?

List the patents, trademarks, service marks and copyrights that have been obtained or applied for and the status of those applications. Briefly describe any licensing, royalty agreements, franchise agreements, distribution rights, trade names, or trade secrets associated with your product/service.

Governmental approvals

5. What governmental approvals are necessary for your venture?

Identify the governmental agencies that regulate businesses in your industry. List the necessary governmental approvals required at the federal, state, and local levels. Some governmental regulatory agencies include the FDA, EPA, FCC, USDA, OSHA, IRS, Secretary of State, your state department of revenue and taxation, Workers' Compensation Division, health departments, and planning and zoning commissions.

Product/service liability

6. What are the possible liabilities this product/service may pose? What are the insurance requirements?

List the types of insurance, amount of coverage needed, and costs to protect key personnel and the company from these types of liabilities.

Related products/services and spin-offs

7. What are the related products/services that will be provided, and how will they increase or enhance the profitability of the venture? What new product or service (spin-offs) could be developed to meet changing market needs in this industry or others?

Describe the related products/services that will be provided. Examples of related services include installation, repairs, and refills. Determine spin-offs (products and services) that can be developed to meet changing market needs in your industry. Explain how you will be flexible in meeting rapidly changing trends and fashions.

Production

8. How much will be produced internally, and how much of the production will be subcontracted out?

Describe the production/manufacturing process. List the costs of production/subcontracting by giving both percentages and dollar amounts. List the variable expenses incurred in the production process: labor (production people), freight-in, repairs, maintenance, and rework.

The Market

The market analysis is critical. Is there a market for the product or service resulting from the concept? Can it be proven? If not, it may be futile to continue the pursuit of this concept. The market for the product/service may be so large and obvious that little needs to be done in the feasibility plan other than proving its size. In the feasibility plan, it is enough to prove that a sufficiently large market exists for the concept and, therefore, further investigation of this opportunity is warranted.

Entrepreneurs need to study their industry trends to determine long-term feasibility of their business concepts. A good example is the market for gourmet and espresso coffee houses and kiosks like Starbucks Coffee. Is this just a fad that will fade away, or will it become a significant trend in the food-service business? Americans have steadily increased their coffee consumption by 2 percent annually during the past five years, and entrepreneurs are adding products from biscotti to T-shirts to lifestyle magazines like the *Coffee Journal* and Internet cafes blending cyberspace and coffee.

Some food-service experts predict that the market for gourmet and espresso coffee is becoming saturated in the United States and will shrink. Others point out that gourmet and espresso coffee houses have been popular in Europe for years and predict that the coffee industry will continue to grow like the wine industry. Whom do you believe?

Look at the wine industry, which has been popular in Europe for many decades but not in the United States until people started traveling more and farmers began growing their own grapes, producing local wines, and introducing them into the marketplace. Today, the wine industry has greatly expanded and is a major industry in America.

Most new business concepts have some level of competition, and if the concept is hot, more competitors will enter the marketplace.

Entrepreneurs should be aware of all competitors in their marketplace. Good information can be obtained by studying the competitors. Astute business owners follow the old saying, "Why reinvent the wheel?" Learn from competitors and then create new ways to make a product or service better and distinct.

It also is important to define the customers, identify various target markets, and determine if the product/service can satisfy their needs. The feasibility plan should explain the way the product/service will be sold to the customers and what kind of distribution channels will be used.

The feasibility plan is simply a gateway that must be passed through on the way to developing a detailed business plan. Bear in mind that many detailed business plans cost time and money to write. There is no need to waste efforts if the concept does not have a sizable marketplace or a definite market niche.

**Formatting The Market section
with section titles**

Current market size
Insert answer to question 1
Growth potential of the industry
Insert answer to question 2
Industry trends
Insert answer to question 3
Competition profile
Insert answer to question 4
Customer profile
Insert answer to question 5
Customer benefits
Insert answer to question 6
Target markets
Insert answer to question 7
Market penetration
Insert answer to question 8

The market questions

Current industry size

1. What is the current size of the industry for the product/service at the national, regional, state, and local levels?

Indicate the number of dollars spent annually by customers and/or units consumed. Cite the source(s) of information so readers believe your statements and projections.

Growth potential of the industry

2. What is the growth potential of the industry for the product/service?

Is the industry expanding, stable, or declining? Identify the life cycle stage of products/services in your industry: introduction, growth, maturity, or decline. Cite the source(s) of information.

Industry trends
3. What industry trends do you predict will affect the product/service?

Predict the effect of technology on future trends. For example, the food industry is concentrating on low-fat, no-cholesterol products as a result of advances in biotechnology and cancer research. Cite the source(s) of information.

Competition profile
4. Describe the competitive advantage for your product/service.

Identify the direct and indirect competition for your product/service. Describe the competitive advantage of your product/service in terms of price, quality, unique features, distribution channels, marketing/advertising, geographic location, strengths/weaknesses, and market share. How are new enterprises treated in your industry? Use the Competitive Analysis Matrix to chart for yourself the competitive advantages of your venture over area competitors. The matrix appears on the following page and on the CD-ROM.

Competitive analysis matrix

Competitive analysis matrix	Price	Production/ quality	Unique features	Distribution system	Marketing/ advertising	Geographic location	Strengths/ weaknesses	Market share
Product/Service								
Competitor A								
Competitor B								
Competitor C								
Competitor D								
Competitor E								
Competitor F								

Customer profile

5.   Who is the intended customer for your product/service?

Describe the customer profile in terms of age, gender, profession, income, geographic location, and other demographics. Include customer psychographics such as attitudes, values, belief systems, hobbies, interests, and social status. Describe business-to-business customers in terms of business type, SIC and NAICS codes, intended use, geographic location, and size of organization.

Customer benefits

6.   What problems are you solving for your customers?

List in bullet form the primary benefits of the product/service. Explain the benefits for the customer in terms of the problems you are solving. Turn features (physical characteristics) and advantages (performance characteristics) into benefits by describing the customer satisfaction that will be derived from the use of the product/service.

Target markets

7.   What target markets exist for your product/service?

Define the number of potential customers for each target market. Estimate the size and potential dollar volume. Prioritize target markets. List the names of customers, companies, or specific groups of customers like market segments.

Market penetration

8.   How will the product/service be sold to potential customers?

Illustrate how the product/service will be sold to potential customers, such as through distributors, sales reps, direct sales force, telemarketing, advertising, promotion, packaging, catalogs, direct mail, customer service, warranties, trade shows, and guerrilla marketing.

Price and Profitability

Will the customer pay enough for the product to make the enterprise profitable enough to be worth undertaking? All too often the answer to that question is NO! The venture fails because it cannot maintain a sufficiently high gross margin to cover expenses and still yield a decent profit.

Remember, the price/cost ratio determines the gross margin. If your immediate customer will pay five times the direct costs, then the gross margin will be 80 percent, since the cost of goods sold will be 20 percent. If sales are $1,000,000, then you will have $800,000 with which to meet expenses and enjoy a healthy profit.

Unfortunately, in their eagerness to go into business, entrepreneurs often wear rose-colored glasses. Entrepreneurs typically start their businesses with a concept in which direct costs are too high to realize a profit. The venture is doomed from the beginning. The market won't pay the price to cover the expenses of the business.

Anyone can sell a dollar bill for 90 cents on the streets. But where is the profit? Consequently, it is essential when writing the feasibility plan to consider the venture's price/cost ratios. One rule of thumb to follow is that the product should sell for at least five times its direct cost. The venture that makes larger profits has a much more favorable price/cost ratio.

The venture's profit possibilities are critical. Does the proposed venture look like it is worth doing? Can you prove it? Just being marginally profitable is not enough to survive in today's competitive environment. There must be a large enough margin for error. If the profitability of the venture is suspect, the entrepreneur should pass on to the next possible venture. Run, don't walk.

In addition, consider whether the economics of the industry meet your personal criteria. For example, if you choose to purchase an ice cream franchise, you'll likely make $35,000 after taxes, according to industry data. If that amount of profit is insufficient to meet your personal needs and goals, then avoid that business venture.

In retail menswear, the entrepreneur can earn about 8 percent profit before taxes. However, successful high-technology companies earn 20 to 35 percent profit before taxes. Where are investors going to place their money? Remember that money seeks its best employment.

The nature of the business generally dictates how much money can be paid in salaries, benefits, and profits. Remember, it is difficult to outperform the well-managed firms in an industry. If your plan is based on doing a better job than your competitor, you are making a serious statement about your comparative management skills. Potential investors will question your assumptions. It is extremely difficult to beat industry averages. Avoid this trap.

Bankers complain that the big weakness they find in most feasibility plans is that entrepreneurs do not properly estimate their start-up costs. There are many costs related to starting a business, such as rent and utilities deposits, fixtures and furniture, computers, signage, office supplies, and insurance. If the entrepreneur has not realistically projected start-up costs, the business could start with a negative cash flow and run into immediate financial difficulties.

Formatting the Price and Profitability section with section titles

Price list
   Insert answer to question 1
Sales estimate
   Insert answer to question 2
Cost of product/service
   Insert answer to question 3
Gross margin
   Insert answer to question 4
Three-year operating expenses
   Insert answer to question 5
Three-year operating statement
   Insert answer to question 6
Start-up costs
   Insert answer to question 7
Start-up expenses
   Insert answer to question 8
Capital expenditures
   Insert answer to question 9

Pricing strategy

For most entrepreneurs, pricing is one of the most overlooked elements when starting a new business, since it is an art and not a science. It is, however, one of the most important aspects of a business, since pricing strategy determines its profits. Many entrepreneurs calculate how much it will cost to make the product or provide the service and then add a percentage to the figure. They fail to let the market determine their prices. Don't set your prices without selecting a pricing strategy that will help you achieve your overall goals.

The prices of other competitive products limit pricing freedom. Both directly competitive and substitute products affect what a business can get for its product or service. In most markets, the buyer confronts an array of products that vary from expensive, top-of-the-line products to cheap junk. All of these items affect a business' price. It will have to fit its product's qualities and features into this spectrum of prices. It is usually difficult to charge more for a product than a competitor gets for a somewhat superior item.

Entrepreneurs can't price in a vacuum. There are factors that govern the price they can get for what they sell, namely the marketplace.

There are several ways to obtain pricing information.

- Call on several potential customers and ask them what they would be willing to pay for your services.
- Hold a focus group with potential customers and ask them about how much they would be willing to pay for different services.
- Talk to other entrepreneurs offering similar services that are not in the immediate geographic area. Ask them what they charge.
- Contact the professional association and ask what type of pricing is standard for the industry. Find out what competitors charge for similar goods or services.

Questions A–F are planning worksheets to help you develop pricing for your products/services.

Price and profitability analysis: Planning worksheet

A.   What pricing strategy will you adopt for your products and services?

Describe the pricing strategy you will use for your products/services. Is your strategy based on economic indicators—called economic pricing strategies. Or, is your pricing strategy based on the cost to produce—called mathematical pricing strategies. Setting prices without a strategy is like throwing a dart at a "pricing" dartboard. It doesn't make any sense. Explain how your pricing strategy will help you reach your overall marketing and profitability goals.

Price and profitability analysis: Planning worksheet

B. How does your price match the strategy?

What will your price range be for products/services? How do these prices match with the strategy that you have selected? Explain.

Price and profitability analysis: Planning worksheet

C. How does your price compare with that of the competition?

What are the prices of your competitors' products/services? How does this comparison match with your pricing strategy?

Price and profitability analysis: Planning worksheet
D.   Are your customers willing to pay your price?

What kind of research will you do to assure yourself that your potential customers are willing to pay this price?

Price and profitability analysis: Planning worksheet
E.   What else do you need to know to make decisions about pricing?

What else do you need to know to confirm your pricing strategy? What do you need to know from the competitors, market, customers, suppliers, etc.? How will you get this information?

Price and profitability analysis: Planning worksheet

F.   Write the formula for your cost of product/service.

For each product/service that you intend to sell, brainstorm a list of expenses that would figure into the cost of products/services, and then figure the cost for each expense for one product or service sold.

List of expenses incurred	$
Total	

Price and profitability questions

Price list

1. How will you price your products/services?

Products/services	**Price**
_____	
_____	
_____	
_____	
_____	
_____	

Price assumptions:

If the venture provides more than one product/service, list each individually. If the venture has many products/services, list them by related categories.

Assumptions: Explain how you determined the price(s) for the product/service. Defend your price list in terms of customer savings, competitors' prices, prices of substitutes, complementary products, the market's perceived values, and distribution channel pressures. Explain how the pricing structure is sensitive to the customer's buying points. Compare your price list to industry standards.

Sales estimate

2.   What is your sales estimate by product/service for three years?

Product/service	Year 1	Year 2	Year 3
Product/service	_____	_____	_____
Product/service	_____	_____	_____
Product/service	_____	_____	_____
Product/service	_____	_____	_____
Product/service	_____	_____	_____
Total sales	_____	_____	_____

Sales assumptions:

If the concept has multiple products/services, then list them by groups.
Include assumptions. Explain how you developed your sales forecast and growth potential. List the number of units that must be sold in order to achieve the sales forecast. Determine the percentage of market share your business will control when the sales forecast is achieved.

Cost of product/service

3.   What is the cost of providing the product/service for three years?

Product/service	Year 1	Year 2	Year 3
Product/service	_____	_____	_____
Product/service	_____	_____	_____
Product/service	_____	_____	_____
Product/service	_____	_____	_____
Product/service	_____	_____	_____
Total sales	_____	_____	_____

Cost of goods sold assumptions:

The cost of product/service includes materials, labor, and variable overhead; however, it does not include operating expenses. If the venture provides more than one product/service, list each individually or by group. Include assumptions. Cost of goods sold is often calculated as a percentage of sales. Retail and wholesale businesses consider the average markup, inventory shrinkage, and freight-in to project cost of goods sold. Manufacturing businesses consider production costs in terms of materials, direct labor, and variable overhead (expenses that directly increase with each unit sold). Service businesses usually do not have cost of goods sold. Refer to *RMA Annual Statement Studies* or another comparison of industry averages.

Gross margin

4.　What will the gross margin be for each product/service for three years?

Product/service	Year 1	Year 2	Year 3
Product/service	_____	_____	_____
Product/service	_____	_____	_____
Product/service	_____	_____	_____
Product/service	_____	_____	_____
Product/service	_____	_____	_____
Total sales	_____	_____	_____

Gross margin assumptions:

The gross margin is the net sales minus cost of goods sold, sometimes termed gross profit. List your gross margin for each product/service. Include in the assumptions the gross margin percentage (margin/price). Use product categories if there are many products. Compare gross margin to industry averages.

Three-year operating expenses budget

5. Prepare a list of operating expenses for the new venture for three years. Write an assumption for each expense.

Marketing expenses	Year 1	Year 2	Year 3
Salaries & wages - marketing	_____	_____	_____
Benefits & taxes - marketing	_____	_____	_____
Commissions, reps & contractors	_____	_____	_____
Advertising - broadcast	_____	_____	_____
Advertising - print	_____	_____	_____
Advertising - direct mail	_____	_____	_____
Advertising - other	_____	_____	_____
Marketing - brochures/posters	_____	_____	_____
Marketing - samples/trade shows	_____	_____	_____
Other marketing expenses	_____	_____	_____
Total marketing expenses	_____	_____	_____

Marketing expense assumptions:

Operating expenses incurred during the first three years of operation should be broken down into three categories: marketing expenses, administrative expenses, and general expenses. Expenses incurred prior to the first day of sales are referred to as "start-up" expenses. Do not include start-up expenses in the Three-year operating expenses section.

Assumptions: Explain how you determined each marketing expense and defend the decision for each expense. The assumptions in the feasibility plan explain how the budget figures were developed. The more factual the assumptions, the more valid the plan. Assumptions should be numbered and these numbers should appear on the matching chart of accounts.

Administrative expenses

	Year 1	Year 2	Year 3
Salaries & wages	_____	_____	_____
Benefits & taxes	_____	_____	_____
Meals & entertainment	_____	_____	_____
Dues & subscriptions	_____	_____	_____
Professional fees	_____	_____	_____
Accounting/bookkeeping	_____	_____	_____
Travel/automobile	_____	_____	_____
Other administrative expenses	_____	_____	_____
Total administrative expenses	_____	_____	_____

Administrative expense assumptions:

Explain how you determined each administrative expense and defend the decision for each expense. The assumptions in the feasibility plan explain how the budget figures were developed. The more factual the assumptions, the more valid the plan. Assumptions should be numbered and these numbers should appear on the matching chart.

General expenses	Year 1	Year 2	Year 3
Bank charges	_____	_____	_____
Credit card fees	_____	_____	_____
Interest expense	_____	_____	_____
Insurance	_____	_____	_____
Office supplies	_____	_____	_____
Other supplies	_____	_____	_____
Postage	_____	_____	_____
Telephone	_____	_____	_____
Utilities	_____	_____	_____
Rent	_____	_____	_____
Repairs & maintenance	_____	_____	_____
Taxes & licenses	_____	_____	_____
Other general expenses	_____	_____	_____
Total general expenses	_____	_____	_____

General expense assumptions:

Explain how you determined each general expense and defend the decision for each expense. The assumptions in the feasibility plan explain how the budget figures were developed. The more factual the assumptions, the more valid the plan. Assumptions should be numbered and these numbers should appear on the matching chart of accounts.

Three-year operating statement

6.   What is your net profit?

Product/service	Year 1	Year 2	Year 3
Sales	_____	_____	_____
– Cost of goods sold	_____	_____	_____
= Gross margin	_____	_____	_____
– Marketing expenses	_____	_____	_____
– Administrative expenses	_____	_____	_____
– General expenses	_____	_____	_____
= Gross profit*	_____	_____	_____

*Before taxes, amortization, and depreciation

Estimate the sales, cost of goods, gross margin, operating expenses, and profit by year for the next three years. You will calculate your net profit in the last question of this section. To be ready, you must be able to estimate your sales and cost of goods sold for three years. Enter the totals from each of the previous tables into the table above. This table is designed to show you the profitability of your venture before taxes, amortization, and depreciation.

Start-up costs

7. What are the costs to start this business?

Start-up cost	Year 1
Petty cash	_____
Register cash	_____
Opening inventory	_____
Rent (last month's)	_____
Security deposit	_____
Telephone deposit	_____
Utilities deposit	_____
Other deposits and start-up costs	_____
Total start-up costs	_____

Start-up costs assumptions:

Start-up costs are items that cost the entrepreneur cash, but there is no tax deductibility—they are not expenses. Instead they maintain value. Explain how you determined each start-up cost, and defend the decision for each cost. The assumptions in the feasibility plan explain how the budget figures were developed. The more factual the assumptions, the more valid the plan. Assumptions should be numbered, and these numbers should appear on the matching chart of accounts.

Start-up expenses

8.   What are your start-up expenses?

Start-up expense	Year 1
Fictitious name costs	_____
Corporation filing fee	_____
Corporation tax prepayment	_____
Activation fee	_____
Legal & consulting fees	_____
Accounting fees	_____
Federal tax ID	_____
Sales tax permits	_____
Salaries & wages: training/setup	_____
Benefits & taxes: training/setup	_____
Office supplies	_____
Business supplies	_____
Printing: cards, stationery, brochures	_____
Pre-opening advertising	_____
Other start-up expenses	_____
Total start-up expenses	_____

Start-up expense assumptions:

Start-up expenses are the expenses of starting your business. Explain how you determined each item, and defend the decision for each cost. The assumptions in the feasibility plan explain how the budget figures were developed. The more factual the assumptions, the more valid the plan. Assumptions should be numbered, and these numbers should appear on the matching chart of accounts.

Capital expenditures

9. What are your capital expenditures to start this business?

Capital expenditures	Year 1	Year 2	Year 3
Equipment			
Furniture			
Leasehold improvements			
Vehicles			
Buildings			
Land			
Total capital expenditures			

Capital expense assumptions:

Capital expenditures are assets that must be purchased prior to starting the business. Explain how you determined each item, and defend the decision for each cost. The assumptions in the feasibility plan explain how the budget figures were developed. The more factual the assumptions, the more valid the plan. Assumptions should be numbered, and these numbers should appear on the matching chart of accounts.

Plan for Further Action

The last section of a feasibility plan focuses on the future. Does the feasibility study indicate that the concept is worth pursuing?

Once the entrepreneur proves that the business-concept statement is feasible and a reasonable profit can be obtained, it is time to proceed to the business plan. This is a big step, requiring a commitment of time, effort, and money.

The feasibility plan may indicate that the concept is worthwhile but not for a new company. Instead, the concept should be sold or licensed to some existing firm.

Many entrepreneurs will use their feasibility plans to show potential investors, bankers, employees, friends, personal business advisers, and corporate strategic partners. Often this type of exposure will elicit useful information to further develop and better focus the original business concept.

A group of entrepreneurs wrote a feasibility plan for opening a new business in a relatively new industry. They took the feasibility plan to five industry consultants to read it, make comments, and recommend whether they should proceed and open the business. The consultants asked them to conduct more research and provide the answers to additional industry-specific questions. The consultants commented that the well-written feasibility plan uncovered additional areas that needed to be researched and addressed.

Too many entrepreneurs start their businesses without thoroughly researching their industries and preparing feasibility plans; then they wonder why they fail. It is critical to write a feasibility plan on any new business concept in the beginning. This process will reveal what further action should be taken on the business concept—either launch a new venture or abort the idea.

Formatting the Plan for Further Action with section titles

Needed capital
Insert answer to question 1
Entrepreneur's role
Insert answer to question 2
Business plan
Insert answer to questions 3, 3a, 3b
License potential
Insert answer to question 4
Corporate partners
Insert answer to question 5
Proprietary rights
Insert answer to question 6
Infrastructure members
Insert answer to question 7

Plan for further action questions

Needed capital

1. How can the needed capital for starting the new venture be obtained? Will you use a bank, venture capitalist, private placement, friends, relatives, or yourself?

Calculate the amount of capital needed for starting the new venture, and explain how it will be obtained. List how much money the owner(s) will invest, how much investment capital will be raised, and how much in loans will be required to operate the business. Identify the traditional sources available for capital: banks, investment bankers, government loans/grants (SBA, SBIC, MESBIC), venture capitalists. Identify alternative sources available for capital: angels, credit cards, private placement, friends, relatives, customers in hand, strategic partners, suppliers, professional advisers, business acquaintances, prospective employees, leasing companies.

Entrepreneur's role

2. What role will you play in the new venture?

Define the role the entrepreneur will play in the new venture: ownership only, ownership and manager, other.

Business plan

3.   Should a business plan be written?

List the key points that should be further researched. Reasons to write a business plan may include creating a management and organizational structure, conducting in-depth market and consumer research, preparing operating budgets and pro formas, developing operating and control systems, and planning for growth. If a business plan should not be written, list the reasons why.

Pitfalls

3a.   What are the pitfalls that the feasibility plan identified? Is it possible to overcome or eliminate all of these obstacles?

Describe the pitfalls and illustrate possible strategies to overcome any or all of these obstacles. List in bullet form how each pitfall can be solved.

Positives

3b. What are the positives or strong points identified by the feasibility plan?

Do not be vague, instead give factual statements. Use meaningful adjectives that are to the point and easy to understand. For example, instead of stating, "The company will have the greatest service," explain how the service is better.

License potential

4. Should the product/service be licensed or royalty rights be given to another company? If yes, why, and who is a potential licensee?

Explain your decision by listing the reasons why. Describe who would be a potential licensee.

Corporate partners

5.   Are there potential corporate partners or joint-venture opportunities?

List names, addresses, and possible contact persons for corporate partners.

Proprietary rights

6.   Do you have any proprietary rights that could be sold to other parties?

Indicate who and estimate the amount of each sale. Include any distribution rights, patents, trademarks, service marks, trade secrets, and franchises.

Infrastructure members

7. What infrastructure members are available to help prepare the business plan? What is the projected cost of their services?

List key advisors, including accountants, lawyers, bankers, and consultants. Consultant areas should include risk management, strategic alliances, computer technology, management, marketing, and specialists in product/service issues. Estimate the cost of using key advisors and any compensation that should be provided (fees, salary, stocks, warrants, other).

Conclusion

After all of these questions and any other additional questions that may surface are answered, the entrepreneur is ready to begin writing and assembling the feasibility plan. These answers can be used as the basis for the plan. Remember, the main purpose of a feasibility plan is to test the business concept and determine whether it should be further developed. If the answer is yes, the entrepreneur must now consider developing and writing a formal business plan. There should be no disappointment if the completed feasibility plan indicates that the concept is not workable or profitable. Think of the money, time, and embarrassment of failure that can be saved by not launching a weak business concept. This is the reason that concept testing and entrepreneurial research and planning are so critical.

Only a small percentage of business concepts pass the test and warrant writing a business plan. Some potential investor or lender may accept the answers to the questions provided in the feasibility plan instead of asking the entrepreneur to prepare a formal business plan.

The Business Plan

If the business or new venture is growing, stagnant, or losing sales, it is time to prepare a business plan. The business planning process is essential to turning a business into a successful venture. The steps entrepreneurs go through in writing a business plan force them to consider many essential tasks that are likely to be overlooked. The very act of writing a plan for the proposed venture will be the most informative part of the process. Definitely, it instills a much-needed discipline to the often overly enthusiastic behavior of the eager-to-get-on-with-it entrepreneur.

The need for business planning and a business plan for a venture cannot be overemphasized. It forces entrepreneurs to consider every facet of the business and place decisions on paper, where they can be evaluated and considered by everyone involved. Additionally, potential investors insist on a business plan. Investors do not want to listen to emotional hype from the entrepreneur. They want hard facts that they can digest at their own speed. They want a document with information they can investigate, as well as some evidence of the entrepreneur's analytical and conceptual skills.

It is not uncommon for an entrepreneur to often abandon a concept rather quickly once into the developmental stage of writing a business plan when it becomes obvious that the concept will not work. People often try to find someone else to write the business plan. Unfortunately, much of the benefit of a business plan is lost if somebody else writes it. Sitting down and developing the plan, section by section, forces the entrepreneur to do considerable thinking, evaluating, and planning. Without exception, entrepreneurs who have written their own business plans report that they were forced to rethink many aspects of their venture. Often, it became apparent to them that there were some serious flaws in their thinking. The parts did not fit together properly.

The business plan is not a blueprint to follow step-by-step in running the venture. Instead, consider it a road map for going in a desired direction. There will be detours and many bad roads along the way. But the entrepreneur will still find the business plan helpful, even if it is continually changing as new information and new experiences are encountered.

Plan every aspect of the business, either formally or informally. One way or another, many decisions must be made concerning what is required in all phases of the business. The following outline provides some ideas of what might be included in a business plan, depending upon the exact nature of the venture.

Sections of a Business Plan

There is nothing sacred about the order of topics, although it does seem logical that most people will want to read the executive summary first. After that, the plan should flow logically in answer to the reader's natural inclination about what should come next.

- Cover page
- Table of contents
- Executive summary
- Management and organization plan
- Product/service plan
- Marketing plan
- Financial plan
- Operating and control systems plan
- Growth plan
- Appendix

Cover Page

The cover page is especially important if the entrepreneur is seeking investors. The cover page includes the name of the company, its address, phone and fax numbers, e-mail address, and the chief executive's name. Many business plans lack this information, and then the reader does not know how to locate the company or who to contact. Nothing will upset lenders or investors more than having to look up a telephone number because it did not appear on the business plan.

The company logo should be displayed on the cover page. You also might want to consider including a picture or sketch of the product. Artwork can be effective when it is relevant to the business concept and professional in appearance.

If the business plan is going to be distributed to several different investors or lenders, number each plan separately and display this number on the cover page. This will allow tracking the number of business plans that are out for review. It also may discourage recipients from copying or widely distributing the plan to others. It is advisable to include a statement such as: "The contents of this plan are proprietary and confidential. It is not to be copied or duplicated in any way."

You might consider having the recipient sign a nondisclosure agreement in which the reader agrees to refrain from revealing the plan's contents or ideas to anyone else. By disclosing information without a signed nondisclosure agreement, you may lose your ability to protect the information through trade secrets, patents, or other types of protection.

Table of Contents

This page should include the sections of the business plan with accompanying page numbers. Don't forget to include this information so readers can quickly refer to particular sections they might want to review. You also might want to consider adding tabs to the business plan for easy referral to the sections contained in the plan.

Also include a table of contents page for the appendix section. After this section's title page labeled "Appendix," include a table of contents listing all the exhibits contained in the appendix. For example, if Exhibit A refers to contracts and agreements, the title page for the appendix would read:

Exhibit A	Contracts and agreements
Exhibit A-1	Noncompete agreements
Exhibit A-2	Franchise agreement
Exhibit A-3	Employment contracts

Business Name

BUSINESS PLAN

Business plan prepared by

Entrepreneur's name

Entrepreneur's title

Company address

City, state and zip code

Best numbers to be reached

Date prepared

Month year

Table of Contents

Executive Summary

The executive summary provides an overview of the business. It contains highlights of the current stage of development of the venture, management team, market and customers for the products or services, marketing plans, how much money the venture needs, and what kind of financing is required.

Since the executive summary is intended to be a brief overview of the entire plan, it should be written last even though it appears first in the business plan. It should be no more than two or three pages in length.

Before writing the executive summary, identify the intended audience of the plan. To whom will the business plan be presented and for what purpose? If a plan has more than one audience, write a different executive summary to highlight specific areas of interest.

Write the executive summary in narrative form using impersonal language. Use your name when referring to yourself in the business plan instead of using "I." Avoid long sentences and phrases.

The executive summary should tell the reader what you want from them. For example, if you are seeking a loan, it should state how much money is needed, how the money will be used, your desired financing terms, and most importantly to the lender, how and when the money will be repaid.

Formatting the Executive Summary with section titles

Venture history
Insert answer to question 1
Venture description
Insert answer to question 2
Venture organization
Insert answer to question 3
Venture market
Insert answer to question 4
Venture operations
Insert answer to question 5
Venture financing
Insert answer to question 6

Executive summary questions

Venture history

1. When and why was the company formed? What is the marketing history of the products and services?

If your business is already operating, you will need to include additional information in the executive summary. Explain the history of your company, including when and why the company was formed. Include a marketing history of the company's products and services. List the company's annual sales and profits. Summarize the overall performance of the company.

Venture description

2.   What business is your venture in, and what is the current stage of development? What is unique about the product or service, and what proprietary rights does the business have?

In this part of the executive summary, describe the venture. Current stage of development may be start-up, initial operations, expansion, rapid growth, or stable operations. Promote what is unique about your product or service, including patents, trademarks, copyrighted materials, licenses, royalties, distribution rights, franchise agreements, and the like.

Venture organization

3.   What form of organization does the business operate under, and why? Who are the key management personnel, and what skills do they have to help the business? Who are the key support groups for your management team?

Describe how the venture is organized. Forms of organization include sole proprietorship, partnership, limited partnership, corporation (S corporation, regular corporation), or limited liability company. Include name, title, and brief qualifications of management personnel (complete resumes should be placed in the appendix). Key support groups for the management team may include accountants, attorneys, consultants, board of directors, advisory council members.

Venture market

4. What is the market like in terms of the industry, the customer, customer needs, product benefits, the venture's target markets, and the market-penetration plan? Who are the major competitors, and what are their strengths and weaknesses?

Give the reader an overview of the marketing plan. Provide a specific description of the market and the potential customers. Identify who the venture is going up against as direct competition. Be sure to use specific facts and figures from your market research.

Venture operations

5. How much money does the venture need for product development, marketing, and operations? Highlight how much money is needed to grow the business and how it will be spent.

Explain the operations of the venture in terms of how much cash is required to operate the business.

Venture financing

6. What kind of financing will the company need? How will the money be paid back to investors? How much money has been invested in the business to date, and where did it come from?

Clearly explain the needs for financing. Identify the sources from which cash will be obtained. List how much money the owner will invest, how much investment capital will be raised, and how much in loans will be required to operate the business. Include both debt and equity financing, methods to be used to pay back investors (stock, warrants, loan payments), and the return on investment for each financing method.

Management and Organization Plan

Strong management is a critical factor in the success of a business. This section of the business plan lists the key management positions, along with a brief description of the primary job duties and responsibilities assigned to each position. It also identifies the individuals who fill these positions. Include a summary of each person's prior business experiences that explains how their skills will contribute to successfully performing these duties. If some of these key management positions have not yet been filled, still include a brief job description, what types of business skills and experiences are needed for this position, and how you intend to recruit and hire such a person to meet the needs of the management team.

This section must establish the credibility of the people on the management team, that is, their ability to successfully operate and achieve the outlined goals and objectives for the venture. If any members of the management team lack needed credentials or experience, then explain how these deficiencies can be overcome with assistance from members of your support groups, such as the board of directors, advisory council, consultants, attorneys, accountants, and so on. You must be able to prove that you have access to all the management expertise you need to operate the venture profitably.

It is important to make an organization chart even if the company is a start-up or small venture. Parts of the organization chart may have the same name in several organizational boxes.

Formatting the Management and Organization Plan with section titles

Management team
Insert answer to question 1
Compensation and ownership
Insert answer to question 2
Board of directors/advisory council
Insert answer to question 3
Infrastructure
Insert answer to question 4
Contracts and franchise agreements
Insert answer to question 5
Insurance
Insert answer to question 6
Employee stock option plan and other
  incentives
Insert answer to question 7
Organization charts
Insert answer to question 8

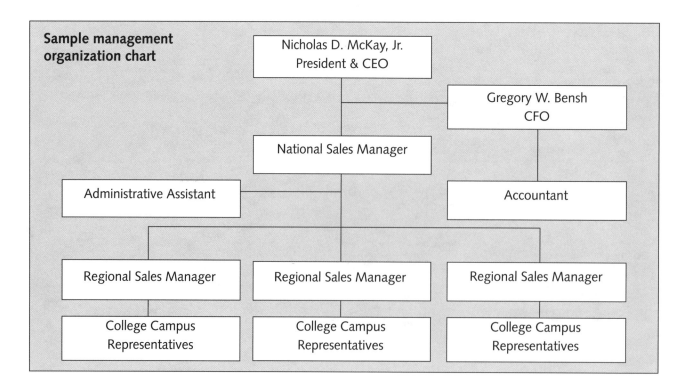

Sample management organization chart

Nicholas D. McKay, Jr.
President & CEO

Gregory W. Bensh
CFO

National Sales Manager

Administrative Assistant

Accountant

Regional Sales Manager

Regional Sales Manager

Regional Sales Manager

College Campus Representatives

College Campus Representatives

College Campus Representatives

Management and organization questions

Management team
1. What is the role or roles of the entrepreneur? Who are the key management personnel, and what are their job descriptions and prior experiences?

Provide a list of the key members, titles, and job descriptions of the management team members. List their experience, talents, training, and special expertise. Indicate that copies of resumes are included in the appendix. Key members might include the entrepreneur, chief executive officer, chief financial officer, chief operations officer, executive vice presidents. Descriptions should include key members' job duties, such as buying functions, selling, quality assurance, marketing.

Compensation and ownership
2. What is the compensation package for the entrepreneur and the management team? What is the ownership, including any warrants or stock options that are owned by the entrepreneur and management team?

Describe the compensation package for the entrepreneur and key members of the management team. List in chart form their salaries, benefits, bonuses, warrants, and stock options. Describe the ownership of the company and whether it is a corporation (S corporation, regular corporation), limited liability company, partnership (limited or general), or sole proprietorship. Indicate if a fictitious business name is registered and being used.

Board of directors/advisory council

3. Who will serve on the board of directors or advisory council?

List in table form the board of directors and advisory council members, including names, titles, addresses, and phone numbers. List their potential contribution, salary, benefits, and any ownership in the company. Identify the officers who hold the positions of chairperson, vice chairperson, secretary, and treasurer. Highlight their qualifications that relate to the business.

Infrastructure

4. Who are key outside advisors, such as accountants, lawyers, or consultants, and what is their compensation package?

List the key advisors including accountants, lawyers, bankers, and consultants. Consultant areas could include strategic alliances, computer technology, management, marketing, and specialists in product or service issues. Include in chart form the key advisor's name, address, phone, and any compensation (salary, stocks, warrants), along with a brief description of his or her expertise.

Contracts and franchise agreements

5. What are the company's management contracts, noncompete agreements, franchise, or other contractual agreements?

Provide a list of all of the contracts for the members of the management team: employment, intellectual property, and partnership/incorporation. Include work contracts, noncompete agreements, franchise agreements, and other contractual agreements. Briefly describe each of the contracts and place copies of the contracts in the appendix.

Insurance

6. If you have a buy-sell agreement, who will be insured in terms of life-insurance policies on key personnel for which the company is the beneficiary?

List the insurance policies for key personnel for which the company is the beneficiary. List the insurance company name, contact person, kind of insurance, and premium cost. Include such policies as life insurance, buy-sell agreements, disability insurance, director's insurance. List product liability insurance in the product and service section. List other types of insurance, such as fire and theft, under operating and control systems.

Employee stock option plan and other incentives

7.   What employee stock option or other incentive plans will be in effect?

Explain the incentive plan using performance goals tied to projected revenues. Define various incentive programs including special recognition awards, lump sum awards, bonuses, stock options, phantom stock, profit sharing, deferred compensation, commissions, and equity sharing. Summarize key points and place the documents in the appendix.

Organization charts

8.   How is the company organized?

Prepare an organization chart showing how the company is organized by person and job title. If a person has not been hired, list job title. Include the number of employees that are in the company. An example is shown on page 56.

Product/Service Plan

Depending upon the exact nature of the venture, a certain amount of information about the product and services must be included. But under no circumstances should the readers be inundated with heaps of technical gibberish. This is a particular hazard among technically oriented entrepreneurs. Do not bog down the business plan with technical details.

Adequately explain the product so the reader will understand it and recognize that the details have been considered and the bugs have been eliminated. Too many plans are written prematurely since the product is not yet ready. Avoid the approach that there are still a few minor bugs to work out. Such statements scare bankers and possible investors.

It is perplexing to know just how much information to include on the product. Consider this question: What will the reader need to know to understand and appreciate the venture? Focus on the benefits or value the product creates. Include technical information and specifications in the appendix.

A word about production

If the entrepreneur plans to subcontract production, the details of those arrangements should be made clear. Consider the following questions: Why will the subcontractor do a good job at the cost projected? Are there alternative sources of supply should the subcontractor fail to perform? The business plan must convince the reader that the entrepreneur will get the needed products.

There is a strong advantage to subcontracting the production, when feasible. There is a tremendous amount of work involved in planning and setting up production of even the simplest items. This time is often more sorely needed for marketing and financing. It is easy to become bogged down in a factory and to neglect marketing efforts and cash requirements.

If the entrepreneur plans to produce the product in-house, two versions of the production plan are needed: one for the entrepreneur and one for the reader. The entrepreneur needs to plan the actual production in great detail; others do not need to read all that detail. They just need to know that it is there to read if they need to refer to it.

Formatting the Product/Service Plan with section titles

Purpose of the product or service
Insert answer to question 1

Unique features
Insert answer to question 2

Stage of development
Insert answer to question 3

Future research and development
Insert answer to question 4

Trademarks, patents, copyrights, licenses, royalties
Insert answer to question 5

Governmental approvals
Insert answer to question 6

Product/service limitations
Insert answer to question 7

Product/service liability
Insert answer to question 8

Related services and spin-offs
Insert answer to question 9

Production
Insert answer to question 10

Facilities
Insert answer to question 11

Suppliers
Insert answer to question 12

Environmental factors
Insert answer to question 13

Product/service questions

Purpose of the product/service

1. What is the purpose of the product or service? How does the product/service benefit the customer? Does it solve a problem or address an opportunity; is it a luxury item or a needed item?

Describe the purpose of the product/service or product/service mix in terms of the problem it will solve. Use meaningful adjectives that are to the point and easy to understand. Include a short list of the products or services provided by the company. Consider using categories of merchandise with percentages of sales to describe the product mix. Include testimonials, results from market surveys, focus groups, and the like.

Unique features

2. What are the unique features of the product/service, such as cost, design, quality, capabilities?

Identify the unique features of the product/service. Describe each feature in terms of the benefit the customer receives or as a solution to the customer's needs. Focus on the benefits or values the product or service creates. If the venture is a retail store, describe the unique features of the store, such as tenant finish, store design and layout, and quality of merchandise. Include any available photographs or drawings of the exterior and signage and the layout inside the store.

Stage of development

3. What is the history of product/service life cycle, and which stage of development is the product/service currently in?

Briefly explain the history of product/service development. Identify the current stage of development. Stages of development include model stage, working prototype, small production runs, full manufacturing/production, other. Provide projected dates for achieving other stages of development. Identify the product/service life cycle stage (introduction, growth, maturity, decline) and determine the projected life of the product/service. Document how the product/service can be regularly improved to remain competitive.

Future research and development

4. What, if any, future research and development efforts will be required?

Describe the future research and development efforts. Compare your efforts to how much money similar businesses in the industry devote to research and development. Project the resources needed for research and development including cash requirements, personnel, facilities, and the like.

Trademarks, patents, copyrights, licenses, royalties

5.   What patents, trademarks, service marks, or copyrights have been obtained? What license or royalty agreements are associated with the product/service, and what plans are there for future agreements?

List the patents, trademarks, service marks, and copyrights that have been obtained. Indicate any patent, trademark, service marks or copyright application and status. Be specific about how all proprietary rights and intellectual property (trade secrets, for example) will be protected. Briefly summarize license or royalty agreements associated with the product/service and any plans for future agreements. Indicate any distribution rights that have been obtained or given away. Highlight agreements and put details in the appendix.

Governmental approvals

6.   What governmental approvals are necessary, and what is the status of such approvals?

Identify the governmental agencies that regulate businesses in your industry. List the necessary governmental approvals required by agencies at the federal, state, and local levels. Some examples of agencies providing governmental approvals include the FDA, EPA, FCC, USDA, OSHA, IRS, Secretary of State, your state department of revenue and taxation, Workers' Compensation Division, health departments, planning and zoning commissions.

Product/service limitations

7. What are the limitations of the product/service, if any?

Provide an evaluation of the product/service limitations. Examples include perishability, limited shelf life, installation needs, legal restrictions. For example, software applications have very limited shelf lives.

Product/service liability

8. What are the liabilities this product/service may pose? What are the insurance requirements and costs?

Examine all possible liabilities this product/service may pose. List the insurance policies for protecting key personnel and the company. Include the insurance company name, contact person, kind of insurance, and premium cost.

Related products/services and spin-offs

9. What are the related products/services that will be provided, and how will they increase or enhance the profitability of the venture? What new product or service (spin-offs) could be developed to meet changing market needs in this industry or others?

Describe the related products/services that will be provided. Examples of related services include installation, repairs, and refills. Determine spin-offs (products and services) that can be developed to meet changing market needs in your industry. Explain how you will be flexible in meeting rapidly changing trends and fashions.

Production

10. How much will be produced internally, and how much of the production will be subcontracted out? What are the costs and services involved with subcontracting? Who are the backup subcontractors and what are their costs? Who supplies the services?

Describe the production process. Identify how much of the product/service will be produced internally and how much will be subcontracted out. List the costs of subcontracting by giving both percentages and dollar amounts of production costs. Include shipping, billing, inventory, stocking, and payment terms. List the company names and contact persons for backup subcontractors.

Facilities

11. What are the plans for facilities (manufacturing, office, retail)? What are the manufacturing plans; that is, the manufacturing facility, production capacity, and future capital-equipment needs?

Describe the need for facilities. Outline manufacturing facilities, production capacity, and future capital required to build facilities. Place detailed information concerning these factors, along with a diagram of factory/store/office layout, in the appendix.

Suppliers

12. Who are the major raw material suppliers, and what are the significant purchasing contracts with them? Are there backup suppliers?

List the suppliers and backup suppliers of major raw materials.

Environmental factors

13. What is the potential environmental impact of the product or service? What steps will the company take to protect the environment? What environmental agencies regulate the product or service?

List any possible problems with manufacturing the product: waste disposal, pollution, noise control, and the like. List any efforts the company will take to recycle paper, metal, and plastics, and to remove asbestos from buildings. Regardless of the size of the company, show how you are socially responsible and environmentally conscious. Note any governmental agencies that regulate the product and service and how the regulations may affect the product or service.

Marketing Plan

The marketing section includes four parts: an industry profile, competition, pricing, and marketing plans.

Almost inevitably, the marketing piece is by far the weakest section of a business plan. That is unfortunate because, in most instances, it is the firm's marketing programs and the marketing skills of the management team that determine its success. Thus in most business plans, the single most important section of the business plan is usually its weakest link.

Several forces combine to create this deficiency. First, marketing is often the entrepreneur's weakest area. Inventors are famous for their marketing ineptness.

Second, and more important, to write an excellent marketing plan you must hit the pavement, get on the streets, talk to people, customers, suppliers, and visit companies. Most of the other sections of the business plan can

be written at your desk. Some phone calls here and there provide most of the needed data. Not so in the marketing plan. You must go out into the marketplace and research the industry. It requires far more time and effort.

Third, marketing plans are not cut-and-dried drills. There are usually many ways to market a product or service, thus many decisions must be made. What is the right way to market the concept? Time and again, entrepreneurs say, "I am now ready to go to market. How do I do it?" People think there are clear-cut answers to marketing problems, and that is seldom so. One often has thousands of alternatives from which to choose.

Finally, many naive entrepreneurs somehow feel that the market will come to them. Build a better mousetrap, and people will beat down the door. You have a better chance of winning the lottery than for that to happen. The business plan must tell the reader exactly how the firm's

---

Formatting the Marketing Plan with section titles

Industry profile
    Current size
        Insert answer to question 1
    Growth potential
        Insert answer to question 2
    Geographic locations
        Insert answer to question 3
    Industry trends
        Insert answer to question 4
    Seasonality factors
        Insert answer to question 5
    Profit characteristics
        Insert answer to question 6
    Distribution channels
        Insert answer to question 7
    Basis of competition
        Insert answer to question 8
Competition profile
    Insert answer to question 9
Customer profile
    Insert answer to question 10
Target market profile
    Insert answer to question 11
Pricing profile
    Insert answer to question 12

Gross margin on products/services
    Insert answer to question 13
Break-even analysis
    Insert answer to question 14
Market penetration
    Distribution channels
        Insert answer to question 15
    Sales representatives
        Insert answer to question 16
    Direct-sales force
        Insert answer to question 17
    Direct mail/telemarketing
        Insert answer to question 18
    Advertising and promotion
        Insert answer to question 19
    Packaging and labeling
        Insert answer to question 20
Service and warranties
    Insert answer to question 21
Trade shows
    Insert answer to question 22
Future markets
    Insert answer to question 23

---

product or service will get into the customers' hands.

Many entrepreneurs note in their business plans that they will advertise in local newspapers and Yellow Pages. However, they must explain why this type of advertising will bring in customers. Detailing how to penetrate the market is critical but often ignored in the plan.

The reader usually is not familiar with the industry, so briefly explain how the industry is structured. Do not make the mistake of featuring the product or service as the focal point of the industry. Explain how the industry works as a whole. Include such factors as the state of technology, how mature the industry is, whether it is expanding or declining, number of competitors, and so on. Most often, industry information is very relevant to a marketing plan. Other times such information is unavailable (if the market is new and just developing) or doesn't apply (if the product or service is a fad or fashion item).

Describing the industry for the pet rock would have been impossible since it had no recognized market. It comes closest to fitting in the novelties segment of toys for adults. It is an advantage if the industry can be measured and described. A product or service has more risk associated with it if the industry cannot be measured.

Marketing questions

Industry profile: Current size

1. What is the current size of your industry?

Describe the current size of the industry for the product or service. Determine the size of your industry at the national, regional, state, and local levels. Indicate the amount of dollars spent annually and/or units consumed annually in the industry. Cite the sources of information.

Industry profile: Growth potential

2.   Is this a growth, stable, or declining industry?

Document the growth of your industry and indicate if the industry is expanding, stable, or declining. Identify the product/service life cycle in the industry: introduction, growth, maturity, or decline. Cite the sources of information.

Industry profile: Geographic locations

3.   Is your industry located in a specific area of the country?

Describe areas of the country where the industry is located. For example, the automotive industry is centered around Detroit and many furniture manufacturers are located in North Carolina. Indicate trends in distribution to different parts of the country and from urban centers to rural areas. Cite the sources of information.

Industry profile: Industry trends

4. What are the trends in the industry? What effect does technology have on the business?

Predict the effect of technology on future trends. For example, the food industry is concentrating on low-fat, no-cholesterol products as a result of advances in biotechnology and cancer research. The Internet is affecting virtually every industry. Cite the sources of information.

Industry profile: Seasonality factors

5. What are the special seasons in your industry?

Indicate special seasons in your industry. For example, the clothing industry has four seasons: spring, summer, fall, and holidays. Many industries are affected by holiday buying patterns.

Industry profile: Profit characteristics

6.   What are the profit characteristics for your industry?

Report on the characteristics of your industry regarding average profit. For example, grocery stores have an average profit margin of 1 to 2 percent on sales. Refer to the gross margin that is standard in your industry. Cite the sources of information.

Industry profile: Distribution channels

7.   What distribution channels currently exist to support the sale of your product or service?

Describe the existing distribution channels through which your product or service can be sold. For example, grocery products can be sold through food brokers.

Industry profile: Basis of competition

8.   What is the basis of competition for your industry?

Explain how your industry competes on the basis of price, quality, promotion, service, or other factors. Cite the sources of information.

Competition profile

9.   What is the profile of the competition? What is your competitive advantage?

Prepare a competitive analysis chart and summarize key points. Compare how your product or service competes in the areas of price, quality, unique features, distribution system, marketing/advertising, geographic location, strengths/weaknesses, and market share. If the company is a start-up, describe how new enterprises are treated in your industry. Use the Competitive Analysis Matrix on the following page and on the CD-ROM.

Competitive analysis matrix

Competitive analysis matrix	Price	Production/ quality	Unique features	Distribution system	Marketing/ advertising	Geographic location	Strengths/ weaknesses	Market share
Product/Service								
Competitor A								
Competitor B								
Competitor C								
Competitor D								
Competitor E								
Competitor F								

Customer profile

10. What is the profile of the intended customer? What are the reactions to the product/service from prospective customers?

If you are marketing to the end customer, describe the individual customer in terms of age, gender, profession, income, geographic location, and other demographics. Include customer psychographics—attitudes, values, belief systems, and social status. Describe business customers in terms of business type, SIC and NAICS codes, intended use, geographic location, and size of organization. List the reactions to the product/service from potential customers. Include any testimonials, results from market surveys, focus group studies, and the like.

Target market profile

11. What is the target market, size, and cost of market penetration?

Identify the target market, describe the size of the target market, and list the costs of market penetration. Define the number of potential customers or potential dollar volume. Note that the target market might not be the end user, but your distribution channels instead. Prioritize this list with best markets listed first. In the appendix, provide a list of potential customers including the company name, address, telephone number, and contact person.

Pricing profile

12. What is the pricing structure? What are your policies on negotiating a price for large orders or on special price deals for penetrating the market? How is the pricing structure sensitive to the customer's buying points?

Outline the pricing structure. Provide a pricing sheet for customers showing purchase price, quantity discounts, shipping procedures, billing procedures, warranties/maintenance contracts. Describe introductory offers and quantity discounts. Defend pricing profile in terms of customers' savings, competitors' prices, prices of substitutes, complementary products, the market's perceived values, and distributive network pressures. Explain how the pricing structure is sensitive to customer buying points.

Gross margin on products/services

13. What is the gross margin potential? What are the industry's pricing policies? Do you differ?

List in table form the prices of all products/services minus their direct costs. Include the gross margin percentage (margin/price). Use product/service categories if there are many products/services. Compare pricing policies and gross margin potential to traditional markups and discount structures in your industry.

Break-even analysis

14. What is the break-even point for your product/service?

Using your business's current fixed costs and sales figures, calculate your product's/service's current break-even point. The formula for the break-even point is:

fixed costs / gross margin per unit

Market penetration: Distribution channels

15. What distribution channels will be used for selling the product or service to the end user?

For distribution channels, list the name and address of the company, contact person, geographical area assigned, and a brief description of the distribution contract. Project costs of aisle displays, point-of-purchase displays, sales promotions, promotional allowances, calendars, catalogs, and the like.

Market penetration: Sales representatives

16. How will sales representatives be used as an approach for selling the product or service to the end user?

For sales representatives, list how many representatives, their compensation package, and description of the contract. Project costs of price promotions, promotional allowances, catalogs, brochures, samples, and the like.

Market penetration: Direct-sales force

17. How will a direct-sales force be used for selling the product or service to the end user?

For direct-sales force, list how many sales persons will be hired, their compensation package (salary plus bonuses, commissions, draw plus commissions), amount and type of training, and support staff members. Project costs of contests, bonuses, meetings, sales aids, displays, samples, training materials, catalogs, and brochures.

Market penetration: Direct mail/telemarketing

18. How will direct mail or telemarketing be used as an approach for selling the product or service to the end user?

For direct mail, list the size of the mailing list, schedule, and estimated response rate. Include an example of the mailer in the appendix. Project costs of mailing list, print materials, brochures, assembly and postage. For telemarketing, indicate whether telemarketing will be conducted in-house or through a contractor. Project the costs and estimated response rate.

Advertising and promotion

19. What advertising and promotion media will be used for the distribution system and end users?

Illustrate the advertising/promotion media to be used for the distribution system and the end user. Media should include press releases, talk shows, and promotions scheduled on radio and in newspapers. Include a specific media schedule with budgets and a sample of any advertising, if possible. For paid advertising, include the cost and projected response rate.

Packaging and labeling

20. What kind of packaging and labeling will be used?

Describe the kinds and costs of packaging and labeling to be used. Identify the supplier/vendor. Explain how these enhance point-of-purchase sales and build brand loyalty. Determine if the packaging is environmentally sound. Include a sample or photo of packaging, if possible, in the appendix.

Service and warranties

21. What warranties and guarantees will be offered?

Provide a brief description of the warranties and guarantees to be offered. Consider the industry standards for returns and service costs for your product/service. Include documents of a technical nature in the appendix.

Trade shows

22.   What trade shows do you plan to use to exhibit your product/service?

List the trade shows. Provide the name of the show, location, date, size of booth, cost to attend, the projected number of contacts, and other information. Make sure to include a plan for follow up with trade show prospects. List trade shows where you plan to attend but not exhibit.

Future markets

23.   What opportunities could occur in future markets?

List the opportunities that could occur in future markets. Include market size, method of market penetration, projected date of entry, and approximate costs.

Financial Plan

It is impossible to assemble any meaningful financial plan until all the other sections of the business plan have been formulated, because the amount of money needed depends upon what the business is to accomplish. Since the financial plan simply represents the dollars required to put the business plan into action, it is important that all the activities of the business plan be accurately portrayed in the financial section. This is the key section for most readers. It reveals all. It is the so-called Bottom Line of the venture.

The answers to four sets of questions (pages 89-90) will appear in the written portion of the financial plan. You will be able to answer these questions as you complete the following:

Worksheets

Projecting start-up funding and expenditures, sales, inventory, operating expenses, a capital budget, and equity and debt is the first step in creating the financial plan. These worksheets will be included in the appendix of the business plan. The last two parts of the financial plan—monthly projections and pro formas—are driven entirely by the worksheet figures.

Assumptions

The second part of the financial plan is the assumptions. The assumptions in the business plan explain how the budget figures were developed. Included in each assumption are the criteria used to determine the budgeted item. Budgets and assumptions are intimately tied together. The financial template includes space to input the assumptions for your worksheet projections.

Monthly projections

Projections provide a breakdown of cash flow and profits by month for three years. The monthly projections part of the financial section includes two of the most important financial documents for the entrepreneur: monthly cash flow statement and monthly projected income statement (before tax).

Pro forma financial statements

The final part of the financial plan is the pro formas. The pro forma financial statements show what the score card for the venture is going to look like for a period of time (income statement), a specific point in time (balance sheet), and the strength of the venture at various points in time (financial ratios).

Most students will be able to use the account categories, or chart of accounts, provided in this planning book. Entrepreneurs typically develop a chart of accounts specific to their business. An accountant can provide a specific chart of accounts.

The financial template uses a conservative approach in its accounting method. One accounting technique that would show a more attractive bottom line and more cash flow is the recording of accounts payable other than inventory and loans.

Accounts payable accounts include wages payable, taxes payable, and professional fees payable. Entrepreneurs can increase cash flow by making these payments on a bi-weekly, monthly, or even quarterly basis as allowed by the recipient. These accounts may appear in your accounting system, but are not used in the template.

The template recognizes expenses when they are incurred rather than when these expenses are paid. Income taxes are estimated for each year and assumed paid out in the following months – April, June, September, and December. This provides the entrepreneur with a more conservative comparison of profits to cash flow. If you use the above accounts payable accounts, or if your accountant requires these accounts, consider illustrating them in your financial assumptions.

Getting started

Projecting accurate financial statements is a process that requires precise attention to detail. Hundreds of figures are first entered into a budget, then transferred to another statement, and finally included in sub-totals and totals to establish the necessary information. Because of this complexity, the financial template (a Microsoft Excel workbook) is included in *The Business Mentor* CD-ROM to save hours of time in producing these financial statements. If you are using the financial template, you may use this workbook to make notes before you enter the information into the electronic financial template.

As you work through your budget projections, remember to justify each item by completing the assumptions for that section.

When you enter figures on a worksheet in the financial template, you may want to view how the numbers link between the other worksheets and financial statements. If you make a change in a worksheet, the other worksheets and financial statements will change accordingly.

If you will not be using the financial template, you will want to take extra care in preparing your projections and financial statements. As an alternative, consider using the financial worksheets in this workbook by entering them into your own spreadsheet program. This helps reduce potential errors caused by incorrect entry and numerous mathematical calculations. If you are creating your financial documents manually using this workbook, be sure to enter your numbers and calculations with care. Check and recheck your totals to eliminate errors.

How to use the financial template

When you initially access the file, Excel may prompt you to "Enable Macros." You must enable macros to use the printing options within the workbook.

The electronic workbook is not designed for columns or rows to be added or deleted. By doing so, you run the risk of losing or corrupting the preset calculations, which have been established in other sections of the electronic workbook.

Throughout the workbook, only enter positive numbers (without commas). The only exception is if you have an established company with a loss in your retained earnings account. That number must be entered as a negative on the Historical Balance Sheet (Set-Up Worksheet).

Step 1: Save the template

When you first open the electronic workbook, give the file another name and save it. This will allow you to keep a fresh version of the template if you want to create another plan.

Step 2: Set-Up

The second sheet in the electronic workbook—Set-Up—asks you to set up your workbook with the name of your company, the year you wish to designate as year one, and your estimated effective tax rate.

Existing Businesses

If you have an existing business, enter your company's current financial position using information from the company's most current balance sheet. The workbook adds the current financial information to the projections to create projected balances for assets, liabilities, and equity. Existing businesses may need to complete a payoff schedule located at the bottom of the Set-Up worksheet. The purpose of the payoff schedule is to record the collection or payment of cash that changes a balance in assets or liabilities.

Step 3: Start-Up

If your company is a start-up, you will want to use this worksheet—Start-Up—to compile the cost associated with starting your business. The start-up expenditures will be automatically included in the financial projections.

Step 4: Enter Your Budget Information

The next five sheets— Sales, Inventory, Operating Expenses, Capital Budget, Equity & Debt —ask you to record budget decisions for the next three years. The electronic workbook utilizes the information you input on these worksheets to automatically generate the financial statements you need to include in the business plan.

Step 5: Print the Financial Projections

Use the Print Options Worksheet to print the Financial Statements to include in the business plan and the Worksheets to include in the appendix.

Financial Plan questions

Sales projections

1. What are your sales projections for the next three years? Where did you get the information to project financials? Are the projections reasonable?

After completing the financial template, provide an overview of your sales projections for the first three years. State the sources of information you used to project sales. (Sources provide credibility to your numbers.) Why are these sources reliable? Explain why you feel the projections are reasonable and accurate?

Income projections

2. What are your net income projections for the next three years? Is your company currently profitable? If not, when will it become profitable?

After completing the financial template, describe your net income projections for the next three years. Briefly describe the sources of information used to project net profit. (Sources provide credibility to your numbers.) Is your company currently profitable? If not, when will it become profitable?

Cash requirements

3. How much cash is required to cover start-up costs, operations, and/or growth?

Explain how much cash the business needs to cover start-up expenses, operations, and/or growth. From what sources will the cash be obtained? When does your business break even as pertains to cash flow?

Sources of financing

4. Based on the cash requirements to start, maintain operations, or grow, will you seek debt or equity financing? How much is the cost of obtaining these funds?

List how much equity the owner will invest, how much equity capital will be raised, and how much in debt capital will be required to start up, operate, and/or grow the business. List the interest rate for each loan. Explain how interest charges are projected to change in the future as loans become secured with equity. Consider a line of credit and other options to save on interest charges.

Historical Balance Sheet for _____

For the year end _____

Assets
Current Assets
Cash & Equivalents _____

Accounts Receivable _____

Inventory _____

Security Deposits _____

Other Current Assets _____

Total Current Assets $ _____

Fixed Assets
Property, Plant & Equipment

Computer Equipment _____

Equipment/Machinery _____

Furniture & Fixtures _____

Vehicles _____

Leasehold Improvements _____

Building _____

Land _____

Less: Accumulated Depreciation _____

Other Non-current Assets _____

Total Non-current Assets $ _____

Total Assets $ _____

Liabilities
Current Liabilities
Accounts Payable _____

Line of Credit _____

Other Current Liabilities _____

Total Current Liabilities $ _____

Long-term Liabilities
Loans _____

Real Estate Loans _____

Other Non-current Liabilities _____

Total Long-term Liabilities $ _____

Total Liabilities $ _____

Equity
Owners Equity _____

Retained Earnings (Enter a negative number for a loss) _____

Less: Owner's & Investor's Draws (Not for use by C Corporations) _____

Total Equity $ _____

Total Liabilities and Equity $ _____

Start-Up Funding & Expenditures

If you are starting a business, you will need to complete the Start-Up Funding & Expenditures worksheet. Record how much money you and your investors will initially put into the venture, the amount you plan to borrow, and the expenditures you expect to make before you open the business. Only include expenditures that will be made during start-up.

Equity Investments includes funds invested in a business by its owner(s).

Loan Proceeds includes funds received with an expectation of the amount being repaid at a later date, usually including interest as well as the principal loan amount.

Real-Estate Loans includes funds received to purchase real estate with an expectation of the amount being repaid at a later date, including interest as well as the principal loan amount.

Security Deposits are not typical costs; they are considered assets because they retain value. These can include deposits necessary to set up telephone and utility accounts, and more.

Rent (last month's) is any upfront payment for future rent that is required from the lessee.

Accounting Fees includes costs incurred during start-up for identifying, measuring, recording, and communicating financial information about a business or organization.

Activation Fee may be charged for new utility or other accounts.

Corporate Fees & Taxes includes costs incurred during start-up for fees associated with establishing the company for tax or registration purposes.

Federal Tax ID includes costs incurred during start-up for fees associated with establishing the company for federal tax purposes.

Fictitious Name Costs includes costs incurred during start-up for fees associated with registering a fictitious name, if applicable.

Insurance includes the cost of purchasing general liability or other insurance during start-up.

Legal & Consulting Fees includes costs incurred during start-up for services provided by legal and other consultants.

Meals & Entertainment includes the costs incurred during start-up for networking meals and other meetings with potential customers and advisors.

Office Supplies includes the supplies purchased during start-up for office needs, not including products that will be resold to customers.

Payroll Expenses includes the entrepreneur's salary, benefits, and company-paid taxes and the salary, benefits, and taxes of all employees. Sole proprietors record their "salary" as owner's draw.

Pre-opening Advertising includes any costs directly related to advertising products and services to potential customers.

Printing (cards, stationery, brochures) includes any costs related to printing or establishing a business image.

Sales Tax Permit is the cost incurred during start-up to obtain a sales tax permit.

Opening Inventory is the amount of merchandise or finished goods the company has on hand and ready to sell to customers at start-up.

Computer Equipment includes all tangible computer equipment that has ongoing value to be used in the business.

Equipment/Machinery is all tangible equipment and machinery that have ongoing value.

Furniture & Fixtures includes all tangible furniture and fixtures that have ongoing value.

Vehicles includes all vehicles used in the business.

Leasehold Improvements includes improvements to leased property, considered an intangible asset to the lessee, which becomes the property of the lessor at the end of the lease.

Buildings includes the building used for the business.

Land is the land used for the business.

Start-Up Funding & Expenditures for _____

Start-up Cash

Equity Investments _____

Loan Proceeds _____

Real-Estate Loans _____

Total Start-up Cash $ _____

Start-up Expenditures

Security Deposits

Rent (last month's) _____

Telephone Deposit _____

Utilities Deposit _____

Other Deposits _____

Total Security Deposits $ _____

Start-up Expenses

Accounting Fees _____

Activation Fee _____

Corporate Fees & Taxes _____

Federal Tax ID _____

Fictitious Name Costs _____

Insurance _____

Legal & Consulting Fees _____

Meals & Entertainment _____

Office Supplies _____

Payroll Expenses (training/setup) _____

Salaries & Wages _____

Payroll Taxes _____

Benefits _____

Pre-opening Advertising _____

Printing (cards, stationery, brochures) _____

Sales Tax Permit _____

Other Start-up Expenses _____

Total Start-up Expenses $ _____

Other Costs

Opening Inventory _____

Capital Expenditures

Computer Equipment _____

Equipment/Machinery _____

Furniture & Fixtures _____

Vehicles _____

Leasehold Improvements _____

Buildings _____

Land _____

Total Start-up Capital Expenditures $ _____

Total Start-up Expenditures $ _____

Sales Projections

To accurately complete the sales worksheet, you will need to understand the potential demand for your products and services as well as the purchasing habits of your customers. What percent of your sales will be cash versus credit? How long will credit customers take to pay and what percent will be uncollectible?

If you sell many products or services, group them into categories for your sales estimates. The worksheet allows several categories. As you detail each projection, consider all the factors that will affect your sales: your capacity, advertising, competitors, seasonality, economic conditions, and so on.

After you enter your sales information, you may want to view other sheets in the financial template to see how the data links to the financial statements. If you change your sales estimates, these sheets will change accordingly.

Gross Sales includes a detailed projection of total sales by product and service for the coming period of time.

Returns & Allowances includes money paid out to customers who return previously sold products and services. This account decreases the amount of income.

Other Income is income received from non-sales activities such as interest income and gain/loss on sale of assets.

Sales (cash) includes sales each month in which the customers pay cash in exchange for products and services. Sales (cash) increase the amount of cash available to operate and increase profit. Sales (cash) increase the income tax amount owed to the IRS. Also include in this category sales to customers using credit cards. Credit card sales will increase the amount of cash available to operate. An expense for using credit cards will be incurred.

Sales (credit) includes sales each month in which the customers promise to pay later in exchange for products and services they receive now. Sales (credit) do not increase the amount of cash available to operate but do increase the accounts receivable and profit. Sales (credit) also increase the amount owed to the IRS.

Received on Account is the amount of money customers pay for previously sold products and services. This account increases the amount of cash available to operate, but is not included in the monthly gross sales.

Bad Debt Expense includes accounts receivable amounts written off as bad debts because customers are unable or unwilling to pay their accounts.

Assumptions: Sales Projections

A. What are all the reasons you believe your sales forecast is accurate?

Write a brief assumption for the Sales Projections worksheet categories that apply to the venture.

Product/Service A _____

Product/Service B _____

Product/Service C _____

Product/Service D _____

Product/Service E _____

Product/Service F _____

Product/Service G _____

Less: Returns & Allowances _____

Other Income _____

Sales (cash) _____

Sales (credit) _____

Received on Account _____

Bad Debt Expense _____

List the many, varied reasons for determining your sales forecast. Explain how you developed your sales forecast and the growth predicted in your sales forecast. Explain the variances between each of the months (for example, season, number of sales days in the month, heavy marketing, exposure, repeat business, expansion plans). Make your forecast believable. Defend your sales forecast by using facts and figures. For each sales estimate, briefly explain the basis for the estimate. For example, an assumption for Returns and Allowances might read, "Estimated at 1% based on industry averages for boutique operations." The source of the industry statistic could be included directly after the assumption.

Sales Projections for _____

Sales Budget Year _____	JAN	FEB	MAR	APR	MAY
Product/Service A_____					
Product/Service B_____					
Product/Service C_____					
Product/Service D_____					
Product/Service E_____					
Product/Service F_____					
Product/Service G_____					
Gross Sales	$_____	$_____	$_____	$_____	$_____
Less: Returns & Allowances	$_____	$_____	$_____	$_____	$_____
Net Sales	$_____	$_____	$_____	$_____	$_____
Other Income	$_____	$_____	$_____	$_____	$_____
Total Income	$_____	$_____	$_____	$_____	$_____

Credit Management

	JAN	FEB	MAR	APR	MAY
Sales (cash)	$_____	$_____	$_____	$_____	$_____
Sales (credit)	$_____	$_____	$_____	$_____	$_____
Received on Account	$_____	$_____	$_____	$_____	$_____
Bad Debt Expense	$_____	$_____	$_____	$_____	$_____

Cost of Goods Sold (COGS) *

	JAN	FEB	MAR	APR	MAY
COGS Percentage	_____	_____	_____	_____	_____
COGS Amount	$_____	$_____	$_____	$_____	$_____

* Cost of Goods Sold is calculated as a percentage of sales. This percentage can be found by researching past performance and industry standards.

Gross Sales = Product/Service A + B + C + D + E + F + G

Net Sales = Gross Sales – Returns & Allowances

Total Income = Net Sales + Other Income

COGS Amount = Net Sales x COGS Percentage

JUNE	JUL	AUG	SEP	OCT	NOV	DEC	TOTAL
_____	_____	_____	_____	_____	_____	_____	$ _____
_____	_____	_____	_____	_____	_____	_____	$ _____
_____	_____	_____	_____	_____	_____	_____	$ _____
_____	_____	_____	_____	_____	_____	_____	$ _____
_____	_____	_____	_____	_____	_____	_____	$ _____
_____	_____	_____	_____	_____	_____	_____	$ _____
_____	_____	_____	_____	_____	_____	_____	$ _____
$ _____	$ _____	$ _____	$ _____	$ _____	$ _____	$ _____	$ _____
$ _____	$ _____	$ _____	$ _____	$ _____	$ _____	$ _____	$ _____
$ _____	$ _____	$ _____	$ _____	$ _____	$ _____	$ _____	$ _____
$ _____	$ _____	$ _____	$ _____	$ _____	$ _____	$ _____	$ _____
$ _____	$ _____	$ _____	$ _____	$ _____	$ _____	$ _____	$ _____

JUNE	JUL	AUG	SEP	OCT	NOV	DEC	TOTAL
$ _____	$ _____	$ _____	$ _____	$ _____	$ _____	$ _____	$ _____
$ _____	$ _____	$ _____	$ _____	$ _____	$ _____	$ _____	$ _____
$ _____	$ _____	$ _____	$ _____	$ _____	$ _____	$ _____	$ _____
$ _____	$ _____	$ _____	$ _____	$ _____	$ _____	$ _____	$ _____

JUNE	JUL	AUG	SEP	OCT	NOV	DEC	TOTAL
_____	_____	_____	_____	_____	_____	_____	$ _____
$ _____	$ _____	$ _____	$ _____	$ _____	$ _____	$ _____	$ _____

Inventory Projections

Many businesses only focus on providing a service and do not sell any products. Some service businesses have a product component. For example, a computer training company may sell training materials. All businesses that manufacture or merchandise products must project inventory costs.

The inventory worksheet takes you through the steps to build your inventory projections. It helps you think through the various expenses associated with your inventory requirements.

Inventory/ Raw Material Purchases (Cash) includes the amount of merchandise or raw materials the company purchases using cash or credit cards. This inventory will be held for the purpose of resale or used to manufacture or assemble into products to be sold.

Inventory/ Raw Material Purchases (Credit) includes the amount of merchandise or raw materials the company purchases on credit terms provided by the supplier.

Payment on Account includes payments made to the suppliers for previous materials sold to the company on credit terms. This account will decrease cash and reduce accounts payable.

Freight-in & Trucking includes costs for shipping and receiving merchandise and materials.

Insurance includes the costs required to cover shop safety and insure equipment.

Salaries & Wages includes the gross amount of salaries and wages to be paid to production people and their assistants (before federal/ state withholding). Include total salary, hourly wages, bonuses, and other forms of remuneration that are subject to payroll taxes.

Employee Benefits includes benefits not usually subject to payroll taxes, including health insurance, disability insurance, and pensions.

Payroll Taxes includes payroll taxes to be paid on salaries and wages, including social security, Medicare, federal/state unemployment taxes, and workers' compensation. Federal/state withholding amounts are paid by employees; therefore these taxes are included in Salaries & Wages and not Payroll Taxes.

Rent includes rental of manufacturing equipment and manufacturing facilities, only. If the production area is shared with office or retail space, the amount used directly for production should be considered. The rest will be included in operating expenses.

Repairs & Maintenance includes amounts needed to maintain manufacturing equipment and manufacturing facilities, only.

Rework includes all costs associated with reworking, or remanufacturing goods, including the costs invested to make products salable.

Subcontracting includes amounts paid to subcontractors for work associated with merchandise or materials.

Utilities includes only utilities consumed in the manufacturing process.

Cost of Goods Sold (for merchandise or products) includes the cost of products sold to customers. As COGS product is calculated, the inventory balance will decrease. A negative inventory means not enough inventory was purchased to cover cost of goods sold. Although the computer may allow one to run a negative inventory, it is not likely that customers will pay for products that cannot be delivered.

Cost of Goods Sold (for production) includes the value added to the product through manufacturing or assembling processes, including labor and variable overhead used to produce the sold products. If the venture is a manufacturing business, include the projected cost of labor and the cost of variable overhead incurred in producing the product. If it is a retail business, include the projected cost of freight-in and other variable costs directly associated with the product. If it is a service business (such as a product installation), include the projected costs for direct labor.

Assumptions: Inventory Projections

B. How did you formulate the estimated inventory you must have in order to reach sales projections?

Write a brief assumption for the Inventory Projections worksheet categories that apply to the venture.

Inventory/ Raw Material Purchases (Cash) _____

Inventory/ Raw Material Purchases (Credit) _____

Freight-in & Trucking _____

Insurance_____

Payroll Expenses - production _____

  Salaries & Wages _____

  Employee Benefits _____

  Payroll Taxes_____

Rent _____

Repairs & Maintenance_____

Rework _____

Subcontracting _____

Utilities _____

Other Production Expenses _____

Explain how you formulated the estimated inventory you must have in order to meet sales projections. List the number of times you expect inventory to turn over in a year. If you manufacture your own inventory, itemize your costs in material, labor, and overhead. For each expense, include an assumption that explains the basis for the estimate. For example, the inventory/raw material purchases of $15,000 for a winery may include the assumption, "15 tons of grapes at $800 per ton and $3,000 inventory to stock gift shop."

Inventory Projections for _____

Year _____	JAN	FEB	MAR	APR	MAY
Inventory Management					
Inventory/ Raw Material Purchases (Cash)	$_____	$_____	$_____	$_____	$_____
Inventory/ Raw Material Purchases (Credit)	$_____	$_____	$_____	$_____	$_____
Inventory Purchases	$_____	$_____	$_____	$_____	$_____

Production Expenses					
Freight-in & Trucking	_____	_____	_____	_____	_____
Insurance	_____	_____	_____	_____	_____
Payroll Expenses - production	_____	_____	_____	_____	_____
Salaries & Wages	_____	_____	_____	_____	_____
Employee Benefits	_____	_____	_____	_____	_____
Payroll Taxes	_____	_____	_____	_____	_____
Rent	_____	_____	_____	_____	_____
Repairs & Maintenance	_____	_____	_____	_____	_____
Rework	_____	_____	_____	_____	_____
Subcontracting	_____	_____	_____	_____	_____
Utilities	_____	_____	_____	_____	_____
Other Production Expenses	_____	_____	_____	_____	_____
Inventory Production Expenses	$_____	$_____	$_____	$_____	$_____

Inventory Balance					
Beginning Inventory Balance	_____	_____	_____	_____	_____
Inventory Purchases	_____	_____	_____	_____	_____
Inventory Production Expenses	_____	_____	_____	_____	_____
(Cost of Goods Sold)	_____	_____	_____	_____	_____
Ending Inventory Balance	$_____	$_____	$_____	$_____	$_____

Beginning Inventory Balance can be found on the Historical Balance Sheet.

Costs of Goods Sold can be found on the Sales Projection worksheet.

Ending Inventory Balance = Beginning Inventory Balance + Inventory Purchases

+ Inventory Production Expenses – Cost of Goods Sold

Make copies for years two and three.

JUNE	JUL	AUG	SEP	OCT	NOV	DEC	TOTAL
$_____	$_____	$_____	$_____	$_____	$_____	$_____	$_____
$_____	$_____	$_____	$_____	$_____	$_____	$_____	$_____
$_____	$_____	$_____	$_____	$_____	$_____	$_____	$_____

_____	_____	_____	_____	_____	_____	_____	$_____
_____	_____	_____	_____	_____	_____	_____	$_____
_____	_____	_____	_____	_____	_____	_____	$_____
_____	_____	_____	_____	_____	_____	_____	$_____
_____	_____	_____	_____	_____	_____	_____	$_____
_____	_____	_____	_____	_____	_____	_____	$_____
_____	_____	_____	_____	_____	_____	_____	$_____
_____	_____	_____	_____	_____	_____	_____	$_____
_____	_____	_____	_____	_____	_____	_____	$_____
_____	_____	_____	_____	_____	_____	_____	$_____
_____	_____	_____	_____	_____	_____	_____	$_____
_____	_____	_____	_____	_____	_____	_____	$_____
$_____	$_____	$_____	$_____	$_____	$_____	$_____	$_____

_____	_____	_____	_____	_____	_____	_____	$_____
_____	_____	_____	_____	_____	_____	_____	$_____
_____	_____	_____	_____	_____	_____	_____	$_____
_____	_____	_____	_____	_____	_____	_____	$_____
$_____	$_____	$_____	$_____	$_____	$_____	$_____	$_____

Operating Expenses Projections

Operating expenses include all of the expenses of operating the business. Some entrepreneurs build faulty projections by merely taking a yearly operating expense estimate and dividing that number by 12. For cash flow purposes, it is critical to evaluate the actual costs planned in the month in which they are expected to be paid. On this worksheet, you will think through all the different expenses required to operate the business. The categories on the Operating Expenses Projections list common types of operating expenses. Because it is easy to overlook some expenses, it is a good idea to show other persons your list to see if they can identify anything missing for your business. Advertising includes any costs that are directly related to advertising products and services to potential customers.

Bank Charges includes any cost of banking for a checking account, merchant account, or other fees.

Dues & Subscriptions includes costs of trade magazines or periodicals and membership dues to organizations.

Insurance is the cost of purchasing general liability or other insurance.

Licenses & Fees includes any costs incurred for occupational licenses, fees, or other licensing registrations.

Marketing & Promotion includes any costs related to marketing to customers or establishing an overall business image.

Meals & Entertainment includes the costs incurred for networking meals and other meetings with potential customers and advisors.

Miscellaneous includes expenses that do not fit into any other category.

Office Expense includes the expenses to run the office, including postage but not office supplies.

Office Supplies includes supplies purchased for office needs, not including products that will be resold to customers.

Outside Services includes money paid for outside consultants, copywriters, and other vendors.

Payroll--Salaries, Taxes & Benefits includes the entrepreneur's salary, benefits, and company-paid taxes and the salary, benefits, and taxes of all non-production employees. Sole proprietors record their "salary" as owner's draw.

Professional Fees includes costs to hire a professional to help with different areas of a business, such as management consultants, lawyers, accountants, and other professionals.

Property Taxes includes taxes paid on property owned by the business. It does not include income taxes. Income taxes are not an expense of doing business (they are not deductible from income for tax purposes) even though they cost cash.

Rent is the specific costs of renting the business facility, including common area maintenance costs.

Repairs & Maintenance includes all costs to maintain computers, equipment, and other capital purchases.

Shipping & Delivery includes costs associated with shipping or delivering products and services.

Telephone includes costs associated with local service, long distance, and mobile phone service.

Training & Development includes costs for employee training and development.

Travel includes costs for traveling for business purposes to training sessions, out-of-town association meetings, or other business purposes.

Utilities includes costs of utilities, such as electricity, water, and gas not used in the production of products.

Vehicle includes actual costs incurred for company-owned vehicles or mileage reimbursement when the vehicle is not company-owned.

Other is included so additional account categories can be inserted and included in the projections.

Assumptions: Operating Projections

C.   What are the assumptions you have made about each operating expense?

Write a brief assumption for the Operating Projections worksheet categories that apply to the venture.

Advertising _____

Bank Charges _____

Dues & Subscriptions _____

Insurance_____

Licenses & Fees _____

Marketing & Promotion _____

Meals & Entertainment_____

Miscellaneous_____

Office Expense (postage) _____

Office Supplies _____

Outside Services_____

Payroll Expenses _____

     Salaries & Wages _____

     Payroll Taxes_____

     Benefits_____

Professional Fees _____

Property Taxes _____

Rent _____

Repairs & Maintenance_____

Shipping & Delivery _____

Telephone _____

Training & Development _____

Travel_____

Utilities _____

Vehicle _____

Other _____

For each operating expense, list the criteria used to determine the expense. Defend the decision for each expense using facts and figures. Provide the factual reasons for determining each expense. Explain why you identified expenses as fixed, semifixed, or variable. Explain which costs can be controlled and which costs might be increased by providers. Explain monthly variances in expenses. Do not straight line expenses by estimating a yearly amount and then dividing by 12 for the monthly figure. For each expense, include an assumption that explains the basis for the estimate. For example, a company that publishes a small magazine included this assumption for salaries, "Designer @ $1750/mo beg. in Aug; Editor @ $60K/yr beg. Sept; Promotions Mgr @ $30K/yr, Ad Director @ $1K/mo + 15% comm., Publisher @ $60K/yr."

Operating Expenses Projections for _____

Year _____	JAN	FEB	MAR	APR	MAY
Operating Expenses					
Advertising					
Bank Charges					
Dues & Subscriptions					
Insurance					
Licenses & Fees					
Marketing & Promotion					
Meals & Entertainment					
Miscellaneous					
Office Expense (postage)					
Office Supplies					
Outside Services					
Payroll Expenses					
Salaries & Wages					
Payroll Taxes					
Benefits					
Professional Fees					
Property Taxes					
Rent					
Repairs & Maintenance					
Shipping & Delivery					
Telephone					
Training & Development					
Travel					
Utilities					
Vehicle					
Other _____					
Other _____					
Other _____					
Total Operating Expenses	$_____	$_____	$_____	$_____	$_____

JUNE	JUL	AUG	SEP	OCT	NOV	DEC	TOTAL
_____	_____	_____	_____	_____	_____	_____	$_____
_____	_____	_____	_____	_____	_____	_____	$_____
_____	_____	_____	_____	_____	_____	_____	$_____
_____	_____	_____	_____	_____	_____	_____	$_____
_____	_____	_____	_____	_____	_____	_____	$_____
_____	_____	_____	_____	_____	_____	_____	$_____
_____	_____	_____	_____	_____	_____	_____	$_____
_____	_____	_____	_____	_____	_____	_____	$_____
_____	_____	_____	_____	_____	_____	_____	$_____
_____	_____	_____	_____	_____	_____	_____	$_____
_____	_____	_____	_____	_____	_____	_____	$_____
_____	_____	_____	_____	_____	_____	_____	$_____
_____	_____	_____	_____	_____	_____	_____	$_____
_____	_____	_____	_____	_____	_____	_____	$_____
_____	_____	_____	_____	_____	_____	_____	$_____
_____	_____	_____	_____	_____	_____	_____	$_____
_____	_____	_____	_____	_____	_____	_____	$_____
_____	_____	_____	_____	_____	_____	_____	$_____
_____	_____	_____	_____	_____	_____	_____	$_____
_____	_____	_____	_____	_____	_____	_____	$_____
_____	_____	_____	_____	_____	_____	_____	$_____
_____	_____	_____	_____	_____	_____	_____	$_____
_____	_____	_____	_____	_____	_____	_____	$_____
_____	_____	_____	_____	_____	_____	_____	$_____
_____	_____	_____	_____	_____	_____	_____	$_____
_____	_____	_____	_____	_____	_____	_____	$_____
_____	_____	_____	_____	_____	_____	_____	$_____
_____	_____	_____	_____	_____	_____	_____	$_____
_____	_____	_____	_____	_____	_____	_____	$_____
_____	_____	_____	_____	_____	_____	_____	$_____
$_____	$_____	$_____	$_____	$_____	$_____	$_____	$_____

Capital Budget Projections

This worksheet shows how to record the purchase of capital assets, depreciation, and money paid to the owner and investors. These budget decisions affect the assets and net worth of the business. Read each step carefully as some assets such as land require unique methods for recording depreciation. Estimating these numbers carefully is important so that an accurate cash flow projection can be computed.

Capital expenditures are recorded as assets on the balance sheet. An asset is an item that retains value. In other words, the item could be sold to recapture some of the cash spent to obtain it. Capital expenditures (assets) are always recorded in the company records at the purchase price.

Depreciation is an accounting method used to adjust the value of a tangible asset to reflect more accurately the current state of the assets in the company. Depreciation reduces the value reported for each asset on a yearly basis. When an asset is purchased, its value is determined by how much it cost the company. The value of an asset generally declines every year the asset is owned or used. This decline occurs because the asset's useable life has been reduced by one year. The book value is reduced, or depreciated, to reflect this decrease in useable life. Asset depreciation methods vary. The objective of some methods is to lower tax liability. For others, the objective is to match depreciation expenses with the revenue generated by the use of the asset. For planning purposes, straight-line depreciation is most common.

Computer Equipment is all tangible computer equipment having an ongoing value that is to be used in the business.

Equipment/Machinery includes all tangible equipment and machinery having an ongoing value that is to be used in the business.

Furniture & Fixtures includes all tangible furniture and fixtures having an ongoing value that is to be used in the business.

Vehicles includes all vehicles to be used in the business.

Leasehold Improvements includes improvements to leased property, considered an intangible asset to the lessee, which becomes the property of the lessor at the end of the lease.

Buildings includes the building to be used for the business.

Owner's and Investor's Draw includes amounts withdrawn by owners or investors in a sole proprietorship. A sole proprietor's salary is considered an owner's draw instead of a salary expense.

Dividends Paid are cash dividends paid as a distribution of profit made to the stockholders of a corporation.

Security Deposits includes any payments such as required by a utility company or a property manager. These security deposits are usually held in an escrow account and are returned in the future. Therefore, they maintain value as an asset even though they are intangible.

Amortization is an accounting method used to adjust the value of an intangible asset, such as the costs to incorporate, to reflect more accurately the current state of the assets in the company.

Land includes the land used for the business. Land is a unique asset because it tends to appreciate in value rather than depreciate. When land is purchased, it is recorded at the purchase price and maintains this value on the balance sheet, even though its market value may increase.

Assumptions: Capital Budget

D. What assumptions have you made about each capital expenditure?

Write a brief assumption for the Capital Budget worksheet categories that apply to the venture.

Computer Equipment _____

Computer Equipment Depreciation _____

Equipment/Machinery _____

Equipment Depreciation_____

Furniture _____

Furniture Depreciation _____

Leasehold Improvements _____

Leasehold Depreciation _____

Vehicles _____

Vehicle Depreciation _____

Building_____

Building Depreciation _____

Owner's Draw _____

Inventor's Draw _____

Dividends Paid_____

Security Deposits _____

Amortization _____

Land_____

Explain the purchase of equipment, furniture, fixtures, leasehold improvements, buildings, and land. Defend the decision for each expenditure using facts and figures. Provide the factual reasons for determining each expenditure. Explain lease versus purchase options, advantages of buying used equipment, and loan values. How will you calculate the monthly depreciation schedule for each asset? One method, called the straight-line method, is to take the purchase price of the asset and divide by the number of months of expected useful life of the asset.

Capital Budget for _____

Year _____	Beginning Balance	JAN	FEB	MAR	APR	MAY
Existing Assets						
Computer Equipment	_____					
Computer Equipment Depreciation		$_____	$_____	$_____	$_____	$_____
Equipment/Machinery	_____					
Equipment Depreciation		$_____	$_____	$_____	$_____	$_____
Furniture	_____					
Furniture Depreciation		$_____	$_____	$_____	$_____	$_____
Leasehold Improvements	_____					
Leasehold Depreciation		$_____	$_____	$_____	$_____	$_____
Vehicles	_____					
Vehicle Depreciation		$_____	$_____	$_____	$_____	$_____
Building	_____					
Building Depreciation		$_____	$_____	$_____	$_____	$_____
New Purchases						
Computer Equipment		_____	_____	_____	_____	_____
Computer Equipment Depreciation		$_____	$_____	$_____	$_____	$_____
Equipment/Machinery		_____	_____	_____	_____	_____
Equipment Depreciation		$_____	$_____	$_____	$_____	$_____
Furniture		_____	_____	_____	_____	_____
Furniture Depreciation		$_____	$_____	$_____	$_____	$_____
Leasehold Improvements		_____	_____	_____	_____	_____
Leasehold Depreciation		$_____	$_____	$_____	$_____	$_____
Vehicles		_____	_____	_____	_____	_____
Vehicle Depreciation		$_____	$_____	$_____	$_____	$_____
Building		_____	_____	_____	_____	_____
Building Depreciation		$_____	$_____	$_____	$_____	$_____
Capital Budget						
Owner's Draw		_____	_____	_____	_____	_____
Investor's Draw		_____	_____	_____	_____	_____
Dividends Paid		_____	_____	_____	_____	_____
Security Deposits		_____	_____	_____	_____	_____
Amortization		_____	_____	_____	_____	_____
Land		_____	_____	_____	_____	_____

JUNE	JUL	AUG	SEP	OCT	NOV	DEC	TOTAL
							$_____
							$_____
							$_____
$_____	$_____	$_____	$_____	$_____	$_____	$_____	$_____
							$_____
$_____	$_____	$_____	$_____	$_____	$_____	$_____	$_____
							$_____
$_____	$_____	$_____	$_____	$_____	$_____	$_____	$_____
							$_____
$_____	$_____	$_____	$_____	$_____	$_____	$_____	$_____
							$_____
$_____	$_____	$_____	$_____	$_____	$_____	$_____	$_____
_____	_____	_____	_____	_____	_____	_____	$_____
$_____	$_____	$_____	$_____	$_____	$_____	$_____	$_____
_____	_____	_____	_____	_____	_____	_____	$_____
$_____	$_____	$_____	$_____	$_____	$_____	$_____	$_____
_____	_____	_____	_____	_____	_____	_____	$_____
$_____	$_____	$_____	$_____	$_____	$_____	$_____	$_____
_____	_____	_____	_____	_____	_____	_____	$_____
$_____	$_____	$_____	$_____	$_____	$_____	$_____	$_____
_____	_____	_____	_____	_____	_____	_____	$_____
$_____	$_____	$_____	$_____	$_____	$_____	$_____	$_____
_____	_____	_____	_____	_____	_____	_____	$_____
_____	_____	_____	_____	_____	_____	_____	$_____
_____	_____	_____	_____	_____	_____	_____	$_____
_____	_____	_____	_____	_____	_____	_____	$_____
_____	_____	_____	_____	_____	_____	_____	$_____
_____	_____	_____	_____	_____	_____	_____	$_____

Equity & Debt for _____

Year _____	Beginning Balance	JAN	FEB	MAR	APR	MAY
Sources of Funds						
Equity Investment	____	____	____	____	____	____
Real Estate Loans	____	____	____	____	____	____
Traditional Loan 1	____	____	____	____	____	____
Traditional Loan 2	____	____	____	____	____	____
Line of Credit	____	____	____	____	____	____
Repayment						
Equity Investment Principal		____	____	____	____	____
Equity Investment Interest		____	____	____	____	____
Real Estate Loans Principal		____	____	____	____	____
Real Estate Loans Interest		____	____	____	____	____
Traditional Loan 1 Principal		____	____	____	____	____
Traditional Loan 1 Interest		____	____	____	____	____
Traditional Loan 2 Principal		____	____	____	____	____
Traditional Loan 2 Interest		____	____	____	____	____
Line of Credit Principal		____	____	____	____	____
Line of Credit Interest		____	____	____	____	____
Outstanding Balance						
Equity Investment		____	____	____	____	____
Real Estate Loans		____	____	____	____	____
Traditional Loan 1		____	____	____	____	____
Traditional Loan 2		____	____	____	____	____
Line of Credit		____	____	____	____	____

Equity & Debt worksheet instructions

Record equity and debt contributed to the business under Sources of Funds in the month it is expected to be received.

Existing amounts should be recorded in the Beginning Balance column.

Calculate the Outstanding Balance by reducing the Sources of Funds amount by principal payments made--not interest payments.

JUNE	JUL	AUG	SEP	OCT	NOV	DEC	TOTAL
_____	_____	_____	_____	_____	_____	_____	$_____
_____	_____	_____	_____	_____	_____	_____	$_____
_____	_____	_____	_____	_____	_____	_____	$_____
_____	_____	_____	_____	_____	_____	_____	$_____
_____	_____	_____	_____	_____	_____	_____	$_____
_____	_____	_____	_____	_____	_____	_____	$_____
_____	_____	_____	_____	_____	_____	_____	$_____
_____	_____	_____	_____	_____	_____	_____	$_____
_____	_____	_____	_____	_____	_____	_____	$_____
_____	_____	_____	_____	_____	_____	_____	$_____
_____	_____	_____	_____	_____	_____	_____	$_____
_____	_____	_____	_____	_____	_____	_____	$_____
_____	_____	_____	_____	_____	_____	_____	$_____
_____	_____	_____	_____	_____	_____	_____	$_____
_____	_____	_____	_____	_____	_____	_____	$_____
_____	_____	_____	_____	_____	_____	_____	$_____
_____	_____	_____	_____	_____	_____	_____	$_____
_____	_____	_____	_____	_____	_____	_____	$_____
_____	_____	_____	_____	_____	_____	_____	$_____
_____	_____	_____	_____	_____	_____	_____	$_____

Financial Statements

The three financial documents every entrepreneur must understand how to read and project are the statement of cash flows, the income statement (profit and loss statement), and the balance sheet. These documents are used internally to answer these key questions:

- Will we have enough cash?
- Can we make a profit?
- Where are we financially today?

Statement of Cash Flows

Much of the financial plan focuses on the development of the cash flow statement, in which all of the money that comes into the business and goes out of it is evaluated. The net result is an estimate of how much money will be needed to start the venture and how much money will be generated by operations down the line.

Cash flow projections disclose to the knowledgeable reader much about the entrepreneur's management skills. If the entrepreneur overlooks significant costs, is overly optimistic or even unrealistic, or gives reason to believe that he or she does not know the costs of running a business, then the reader will most likely conclude that he or she does not know how to manage a business. Seldom can an inexperienced person develop a realistic cash flow statement without considerable deliberation and assistance from others.

A cash flow statement is built from information already contained in the budgets. To build a cash flow statement, start with the beginning cash balance. For each month, add in all of the cash receipts and subtract out all of the cash disbursements. Net cash flow is calculated as total cash receipts minus total cash disbursed for the month. The ending cash balance is a running total of the cash on hand.

Entrepreneurs need to develop a cash flow plan for a time period that is long enough to show the cash break-even point. This is the point at which no additional capital is needed, and perhaps, the point at which investors will get their money back. The cash flow plan is often detailed by months until the venture creates positive cash flow (usually 12 to 24 months).

Income Statement (Profit and Loss)

The purpose of the projected monthly income statement is to determine the net income of the venture before taxes. It is highly possible to show a tremendous profit and still run out of cash. It is also possible to generate a large amount of cash and not make a profit because of incurred debt and other liabilities. The entrepreneur must use both the cash flow statement and the projected monthly income statement as basic tools for sound financial planning.

The projected monthly income statement is built from information already contained in the budgets. To build a monthly income statement, enter the monthly totals from each budget. Record sales from the sales worksheet, cost of goods sold from the inventory worksheet, and expense items from the other worksheets.

Balance Sheet

The income statement reflects the company's income, but note that the income statement says little about how much the company is worth. If the company owns a building (an asset), it probably still owes money to the bank (a liability), and of course, the company may have some retained earnings (equity); none of these are reflected in the income statement. The balance sheet shows the tangible worth of a company. It is a reflection of how much the company owns and how much is due to it and how much it owes to both creditors and the owners. It shows the company's assets, the liabilities, and the owner's equity.

The assets are divided into current assets (cash) and fixed assets (plant and equipment). The liabilities are divided into current liabilities (less than one year) and long-term debt. The stockholders' equity is the difference between assets and liabilities.

Preparing financial statements

If you are using the financial template in *The Business Mentor* CD-ROM, the financial statements are automatically generated from the projections you entered in the worksheets. You may want to review these projections to make sure the information still accurately describes your intentions. Then, to print the financial statements, use the Print Options Worksheet feature in the template.

If you will not be using the financial template to prepare your financial statements, you will want to take extra care in preparing these reports. If possible, use the worksheets in this workbook to recreate the financial statements in your own spreadsheet program. This will help reduce potential errors that can be caused by incorrect entry and numerous mathematical calculations. If you are creating your financial statements manually using this workbook, be sure to enter your numbers and calculations with care. You will need to check and recheck your totals to eliminate errors. If possible, have someone familiar with financial statements review your work for completeness and accuracy.

Financial projections in the business plan

Include the following financial statements in the business plan:
- Monthly Income Statement
- Monthly Cash Flow Statement
- Year-End Income Statement
- Year-End Balance Sheet
- Financial Analysis/Ratios

The worksheets used to project this financial information are also a useful resource for the business plan. Include the following worksheets that apply to your business, along with your assumptions, in the appendix:
- Historical Balance Sheet
- Start-up Funding & Expenditures
- Sales Projections
- Inventory Projections
- Operating Expenses Projections
- Capital Budget Projections
- Equity & Debt Worksheet
- Amortization Schedule

Monthly Income Statement for _____

Year _____	Pre Start-up JAN	FEB	MAR	APR	MAY
Net Sales (less returns & allowences)	_____ _____	_____	_____	_____	_____
Costs of Goods Sold	_____ _____	_____	_____	_____	_____
Gross Income	$_____ $_____	$_____	$_____	$_____	$_____

Operating Expenses

Advertising	_____ _____	_____	_____	_____	_____
Bad Debt Expense	_____ _____	_____	_____	_____	_____
Bank Charges	_____ _____	_____	_____	_____	_____
Depreciation & Amortization	_____ _____	_____	_____	_____	_____
Dues & Subscriptions	_____ _____	_____	_____	_____	_____
Insurance	_____ _____	_____	_____	_____	_____
Licenses & Fees	_____ _____	_____	_____	_____	_____
Marketing & Promotion	_____ _____	_____	_____	_____	_____
Meals & Entertainment	_____ _____	_____	_____	_____	_____
Miscellaneous	_____ _____	_____	_____	_____	_____
Office Expense	_____ _____	_____	_____	_____	_____
Office Supplies	_____ _____	_____	_____	_____	_____
Outside Services	_____ _____	_____	_____	_____	_____
Payroll Expenses	_____ _____	_____	_____	_____	_____
Salaries & Wages	_____ _____	_____	_____	_____	_____
Payroll Taxes	_____ _____	_____	_____	_____	_____
Benefits	_____ _____	_____	_____	_____	_____
Professional Fees	_____ _____	_____	_____	_____	_____
Property Taxes	_____ _____	_____	_____	_____	_____
Rent	_____ _____	_____	_____	_____	_____
Repairs & Maintenance	_____ _____	_____	_____	_____	_____
Shipping & Delivery	_____ _____	_____	_____	_____	_____
Telephone	_____ _____	_____	_____	_____	_____
Training & Development	_____ _____	_____	_____	_____	_____
Travel	_____ _____	_____	_____	_____	_____
Utilities	_____ _____	_____	_____	_____	_____
Vehicle	_____ _____	_____	_____	_____	_____
Other _____	_____ _____	_____	_____	_____	_____
Other _____	_____ _____	_____	_____	_____	_____
Other _____	_____ _____	_____	_____	_____	_____
Total Operating Expenses	$_____ $_____	$_____	$_____	$_____	$_____

Operating Income	$_____ $_____	$_____	$_____	$_____	$_____
Interest Expense	_____ _____	_____	_____	_____	_____
Other Income (interest, royalties, etc.)	_____ _____	_____	_____	_____	_____
Income Before Taxes	$_____ $_____	$_____	$_____	$_____	$_____

Make copies for years two and three.

JUNE	JUL	AUG	SEP	OCT	NOV	DEC	TOTAL
							$_____
							$_____
$_____	$_____	$_____	$_____	$_____	$_____	$_____	$_____
							$_____
							$_____
							$_____
							$_____
							$_____
							$_____
							$_____
							$_____
							$_____
							$_____
							$_____
							$_____
							$_____
							$_____
							$_____
							$_____
							$_____
							$_____
							$_____
							$_____
							$_____
							$_____
							$_____
							$_____
							$_____
							$_____
							$_____
							$_____
							$_____
							$_____
							$_____
							$_____
							$_____
							$_____
							$_____
							$_____
$_____	$_____	$_____	$_____	$_____	$_____	$_____	$_____
$_____	$_____	$_____	$_____	$_____	$_____	$_____	$_____
							$_____
							$_____
$_____	$_____	$_____	$_____	$_____	$_____	$_____	$_____

Cash Flow Statement for _____

Year _____	Pre Start-up JAN	FEB	MAR	APR	MAY
Cash In					
Cash Sales					
Collections from Accounts Receivables					
Equity Received					
Loans Received					
Other Cash In (receipts from other assets)					
Other Cash In (interest, royalties etc.)					
Total Cash In	$_____	$_____	$_____	$_____	$_____	$_____
Total Cash Available	$_____	$_____	$_____	$_____	$_____	$_____
Cash Out					
Inventory Expenditures					
Inventory/Raw Material (Cash)					
Inventory/Raw Material (Paid on Account)					
Production Expenses					
Operating Expenses *					
Paid on Account					
Non-operating Costs					
Capital Purchases					
Estimated Income Tax Payments					
Interest Payments					
Loan Principal Payments					
Ownter's Draw					
Other Cash Out					
Total Cash Out	$_____	$_____	$_____	$_____	$_____	$_____
Monthly Cash Flow	$_____	$_____	$_____	$_____	$_____	$_____
**Beginning Cash Balance **	$_____	$_____	$_____	$_____	$_____	$_____
Ending Cash Balance	$_____	$_____	$_____	$_____	$_____	$_____

*   See Monthly Income Statement for detailed Operating Expenses.

**   Beginning Cash Balance for Pre Start-up can be found in Total Start-up Cash on the Start-Up Funding & Expenditures worksheet. Ongoing Beginning Cash Balances are taken from the previous month's Ending Cash Balance on this worksheet.

JUNE	JUL	AUG	SEP	OCT	NOV	DEC	TOTAL
_____	_____	_____	_____	_____	_____	_____	$_____
_____	_____	_____	_____	_____	_____	_____	$_____
_____	_____	_____	_____	_____	_____	_____	$_____
_____	_____	_____	_____	_____	_____	_____	$_____
_____	_____	_____	_____	_____	_____	_____	$_____
_____	_____	_____	_____	_____	_____	_____	$_____
$_____	$_____	$_____	$_____	$_____	$_____	$_____	$_____
$_____	$_____	$_____	$_____	$_____	$_____	$_____	$_____
_____	_____	_____	_____	_____	_____	_____	$_____
_____	_____	_____	_____	_____	_____	_____	$_____
_____	_____	_____	_____	_____	_____	_____	$_____
_____	_____	_____	_____	_____	_____	_____	$_____
_____	_____	_____	_____	_____	_____	_____	$_____
_____	_____	_____	_____	_____	_____	_____	$_____
_____	_____	_____	_____	_____	_____	_____	$_____
_____	_____	_____	_____	_____	_____	_____	$_____
_____	_____	_____	_____	_____	_____	_____	$_____
_____	_____	_____	_____	_____	_____	_____	$_____
_____	_____	_____	_____	_____	_____	_____	$_____
_____	_____	_____	_____	_____	_____	_____	$_____
_____	_____	_____	_____	_____	_____	_____	$_____
$_____	$_____	$_____	$_____	$_____	$_____	$_____	$_____
$_____	$_____	$_____	$_____	$_____	$_____	$_____	$_____
$_____	$_____	$_____	$_____	$_____	$_____	$_____	$_____
$_____	$_____	$_____	$_____	$_____	$_____	$_____	$_____

Income Statement Projected for _____

	Year_____	Year_____	Year_____
Net Sales (less returns & allowences)	_____	_____	_____
Costs of Goods Sold	_____	_____	_____
Gross Income	$ _____	$ _____	$ _____

Operating Expenses

Advertising	_____	_____	_____
Bank Charges	_____	_____	_____
Dues & Subscriptions	_____	_____	_____
Insurance	_____	_____	_____
Licenses & Fees	_____	_____	_____
Marketing & Promotion	_____	_____	_____
Meals & Entertainment	_____	_____	_____
Miscellaneous	_____	_____	_____
Office Expense (postage)	_____	_____	_____
Office Supplies	_____	_____	_____
Outside Services	_____	_____	_____
Payroll Expenses	_____	_____	_____
Salaries & Wages	_____	_____	_____
Payroll Taxes	_____	_____	_____
Benefits	_____	_____	_____
Professional Fees	_____	_____	_____
Property Taxes	_____	_____	_____
Rent	_____	_____	_____
Repairs & Maintenance	_____	_____	_____
Shipping & Delivery	_____	_____	_____
Telephone	_____	_____	_____
Training & Development	_____	_____	_____
Travel	_____	_____	_____
Utilities	_____	_____	_____
Vehicle	_____	_____	_____
Other _____	_____	_____	_____
Other _____	_____	_____	_____
Other _____	_____	_____	_____
Total Operating Expenses	$_____	$_____	$_____
Operating Income	$_____	$_____	$_____
Interest Expense	_____	_____	_____
Other Income (interest, royalties, etc.)	_____	_____	_____
Income Before Taxes	$_____	$_____	$_____
Income Taxes (if C Corp)	_____	_____	_____
Net Income	$_____	$_____	$_____

Balance Sheet Projected for _____

	Year_____	Year_____	Year_____
Assets			
Current Assets			
Cash & Equivalents	_____	_____	_____
Accounts Receivable	_____	_____	_____
Inventory	_____	_____	_____
Security Deposits	_____	_____	_____
Other Current Assets	_____	_____	_____
Total Current Assets	$_____	$_____	$_____
Fixed Assets			
Property, Plant & Equipment	_____	_____	_____
Less: Accumulated Depreciation	_____	_____	_____
Other Non-current Assets	_____	_____	_____
Total Non-current Assets	$_____	$_____	$_____
Total Assets	$_____	$_____	$_____
Liabilities			
Current Liabilities			
Accounts Payable	_____	_____	_____
Line of Credit	_____	_____	_____
Other Current Liabilities	_____	_____	_____
Total Current Liabilities	$_____		
Long-term Liabilities			
Loans	_____	_____	_____
Real Estate Loans	_____	_____	_____
Other Non-current Liabilities	_____	_____	_____
Total Long-term Liabilities	$_____		
Total Liabilities	$_____	$_____	$_____
Equity			
Owners Equity	_____	_____	_____
Retained Earnings	_____	_____	_____
Less: Owner's & Investor's Draws	_____	_____	_____
Total Equity	$_____	$_____	$_____
Total Liabilities and Equity	$_____	$_____	$_____

Ratio Analysis for _____

	Year_____	Year_____	Year_____
Profitability Ratios			

Gross Margin

$$\frac{\text{Gross Income}}{\text{Net Sales}}$$

	_____	_____	_____

Operating Margin

$$\frac{\text{Operating Income}}{\text{Net Sales}}$$

	_____	_____	_____

Net Margin

$$\frac{\text{Net Income}}{\text{Net Sales}}$$

	_____	_____	_____

Return on Assets (ROA)

$$\frac{\text{Net Income}}{\text{Total Assets}}$$

	_____	_____	_____

Liquidity Ratios

Current Ratio

$$\frac{\text{Total Current Assets}}{\text{Total Current Liabilities}}$$

	_____	_____	_____

Quick Ratio

$$\frac{\text{Current Assets} - \text{Inventory}}{\text{Current Liabilities}}$$

	_____	_____	_____

Gross Income can be found on the Income Statement.
Inventory can be found on the Balance Sheet.
Net Income can be found on the Income Statement.
Net Sales can be found on the Income Statement.
Operating Income can be found on the Income Statement.
Total Assets can be found on the Balance Sheet.
Total Current Assets can be found on the Balance Sheet.
Total Current Liabilities can be found on the Balance Sheet.

	Year_____	Year_____	Year_____

Risk Ratios

Debt Ratio

_____
Total Liabilities
_____
Total Assets

Debt to Equity

_____
Total Liabilities
_____
Total Equity

Efficiency Ratios

Inventory Turnover

_____
Costs of Goods Sold
_____
Inventory

Days Sales Outstanding (DSO)

_____
Accounts Receivable
_____
Net Sales / 365

Investment Turnover Ratio

_____
Net Sales
_____
Total Assets

Accounts Receivable can be found on the Balance Sheet.
Cost of Goods Sold can be found on the Income Statement.
Inventory can be found on the Balance Sheet.
Net Sales can be found on the Income Statement.
Total Assets can be found on the Balance Sheet.
Total Equity can be found on the Balance Sheet.
Total Liabilities can be found on the Balance Sheet.

Operating and Control Systems Plan

The Operating and control systems section contains three major areas: controlling operations; schedule or critical path management; and contingency plan.

In controlling operations, it is necessary for entrepreneurs to show that they understand the nature and importance of administrative policies, procedures, and controls. The operating system ensures that every detail is considered and planned for. Controlling the operating system is critical to the profit performance of the venture.

In scheduling, entrepreneurs need a timetable (sometimes called critical path management). By developing a schedule, it is possible to determine if the venture is on target.

Time is critical, and often the time advantage is what makes a venture successful in the marketplace. Entrepreneurs must recognize the sequence of events that must take place for the venture to be successful; then the planning process must continue.

Contingency plans let the interested readers know that the venture has been thoroughly thought through and that there are other options if the venture runs into some problem areas. Entrepreneurs make multiple assumptions in running any enterprise. If any of these assumptions proves to be erroneous, problems will occur. Since it is common for some assumptions to be erroneous, it is important to have a fallback position for each assumption.

Formatting the Operating and Control Systems Plan with section titles

Administrative policy, procedures, and controls
Receiving orders
Insert answer to question 1
Billing customers
Insert answer to question 2
Paying suppliers
Insert answer to question 3
Collecting accounts receivable
Insert answer to question 4
Reporting to management
Insert answer to question 5
Staff development
Insert answer to question 6
Inventory control
Insert answer to question 7
Handling warranties and returns
Insert answer to question 8
Monitoring the company budgets
Insert answer to question 9
Security systems
Insert answer to question 10

Documents and paper flow
Insert answer to question 11
Planning chart
Product/service development
Insert answer to question 12
Manufacturing
Insert answer to question 13
Financial requirements
Insert answer to question 14
Marketing flow chart
Insert answer to question 15
Market penetration
Insert answer to question 16
Management and infrastructure
Insert answer to question 17
Risk analysis
Insert answer to question 18
Salvaging assets
Insert answer to question 19

Operating and control systems questions

Administrative policy, procedures, and controls: Receiving orders

1.   What administrative policies, procedures, and controls will be used for receiving orders?

Explain how orders are processed after being received. Include a copy of the order form in the appendix. Describe what type of database will be created to keep track of customer information.

Administrative policy, procedures, and controls: Billing customers

2.   What administrative policies, procedures, and controls will be used for billing the customers?

Explain how billing procedures will be set up. Include the billing period, billing format, and the like. Consider placing a copy of billing correspondence in the appendix.

Administrative policy, procedures, and controls: Paying suppliers

3. What administrative policies, procedures, and controls will be used for paying the suppliers?

Identify procedures for controlling due dates on bills. List accounting and bookkeeping controls that are needed in addition to paying the suppliers.

Administrative policy, procedures, and controls: Collecting accounts receivable

4. What administrative policies, procedures, and controls will be used for collecting the accounts receivable? Will you have a separate collection department? Use a collection agency? Use factoring?

Choose whether to collect, have a separate collections department, or hire a collections service. Consider using a collection agency and factoring to increase cash flow and reduce bad debts.

Administrative policy, procedures, and controls: Reporting to management

5. What administrative policies, procedures, and controls will be used for reporting to management?

Explain the communication process for employees to report incidents to management. Describe the format and schedule to be used for management meetings, who will attend, and how often meetings will be held. List the types of reports to be used.

Administrative policy, procedures, and controls: Staff development

6. What administrative policies, procedures, and controls will be used for staff development?

Explain provisions for employee training, promotions, and incentives. Choose among using outside consultants, providing in-house training, and inviting manufacturer representatives for training. List the bonus systems you will use to motivate staff.

Administrative policy, procedures, and controls: Inventory control

7. What administrative policies, procedures, and controls will be used to control inventory?

Briefly describe the system used to establish inventory control. Select whether the system will be manual or computerized. Identify at what point the use of technology will be cost-efficient to control inventory.

Administrative policy, procedures, and controls: Handling warranties and returns

8. What administrative policies, procedures, and controls will be used for handling warranties and returns?

Explain the process for handling warranties and how returns are to be documented for proper credit. Identify a system to handle customer complaints. Also, identify how feedback from customers will be used to improve customer service and product development.

Administrative policy, procedures, and controls: Monitoring the company budgets

9.　What administrative policies, procedures, and controls will be used to monitor the company budgets?

Explain how often budget information is updated for review. Set up budgetary controls for travel, phone usage, photocopies, supplies, and car allowance.

Administrative policy, procedures, and controls: Security systems

10.　What administrative policies, procedures, and controls will be used for providing security for the business?

Describe how you will protect customer lists and trade secrets. Describe the security available for the building and employees. Explain the procedures for protecting company files and backing up computer information. Include plans of action in case of emergency: fire, tornado or hurricanes.

Documents and paper flow

11. What will be the flow of information throughout the system? What documents are needed to prepare for a transaction?

Diagram the flow of information throughout the system. List the documents needed to prepare for a transaction. Identify all the things that should happen to a transaction. Include examples of such forms as invoices, sales tickets, and charge documents in the appendix.

Planning chart: Product/service development

12. When will the product/service be ready to market?

Identify when the product/service will be ready for market. List all the activities necessary to develop the product/service, the names of the persons responsible for each activity, and completion date. Outline the timing of events by month for a minimum of 12 months.

Planning chart: Manufacturing

13. What is the production schedule?

Provide the production schedule. List all the activities that make up the production schedule, the names of the persons responsible for each activity, and completion dates. Outline the timing of events by month for a minimum of 12 months.

Planning chart: Financial requirements

14. When will the money be needed?

List what type of money is needed to finance the project, who will provide the money, and the date the money is needed. Consider listing the dates when payments will be made on financing, when dividends will be declared, and the like.

Planning chart: Marketing flow chart

15. When will the advertising be placed, brochures developed, and the like?

List when marketing activities will be carried out, the persons responsible for each activity, and the completion dates. Outline the timing of events by month for a minimum of 12 months.

Planning chart: Market penetration

16. What is the schedule for market penetration?

List the activities for penetrating the market, who is responsible for each activity, and when each activity is to be completed. Outline the timing of events by month for a minimum of 12 months. Include when you will handle sales-force training, sales-calls schedules, selecting distributors, selecting manufacturers' representatives, and any other pertinent information.

Planning chart: Management and infrastructure

17. When will additional management team be hired and in what order? When will the infrastructure be used and for what period of time?

List when additional management and infrastructure persons will be brought on board, who is responsible for hiring, and for what period of time.

Risk analysis

18. What are the potential problems, risks, and other possible negative factors that the venture might face?

Design innovative approaches to solve these possible problems: sales projections prove wrong, unfavorable industry development occurs, manufacturing costs become too high, competition destroys marketplace (price war ensues), needed labor is unavailable, supply deficiencies develop, needed capital is unavailable, government interference arises, product/service liability occurs, problems with management or personnel arise, product/service development takes longer than anticipated, union problems arise.

Salvaging assets

19. What could be salvaged or recovered if any of the above risks do materialize and make the venture unsuccessful?

List what could be salvaged or recovered if any of the risk analysis events do materialize. Value the assets at what the banker/investor could sell them for within 30 days. Include patents, inventory, accounts receivable, equipment, office furniture, customer lists.

Growth Plan

The purpose of the growth section of the business plan is to forecast as accurately as possible what will be needed by the venture in the future and to make initial plans for accommodating this forecast. Make sure that the growth section agrees with the multiyear projections in the financial section.

Investors, banks, and other interested readers should understand the plans for continued expansion of the venture. They want some assurance that the entrepreneur isn't betting on a one-trick pony. If the entrepreneur is seeking outside money, the investors must be able to see an attractive upside potential. They want to see a few large potential markets in the future.

It is very difficult to accurately project the future in a growth plan. However, make sure that the assumptions for the growth plan are as precise as possible and that they contain sufficient documentation to support the projections.

Many entrepreneurs project the future by just increasing sales 10 percent each year without increasing expenses accordingly. Instead, growth projections should be based on realistic figures that have been developed while researching the market and the industry. Document wherever possible what others are saying about the growth potential of your kind of venture and the industry.

Formatting the Growth Plan with section titles

New offerings to market
   Insert answer to question 1
Capital requirements
   Insert answer to question 2
Personnel requirements
   Insert answer to question 3
Exit strategy
   Insert answer to question 4

Growth questions

New offerings to market

1. What new products/services, store locations, distribution centers will the venture pursue in the future? What new marketplaces will each of the new products/services penetrate? What will be the projected revenues from the new products/services, store locations, and distribution centers for the next three to five years?

List products/services, locations, distribution centers, and marketplaces that will be pursued in the future. Project revenues for three years. Include estimated potential costs. Use chart form or maps to describe new markets to be penetrated. Describe methods of market penetration based on growth.

Capital requirements

2. What are the financial requirements for pursuing the new products, store locations, and distribution centers? How will you raise the needed capital for future growth?

List the estimated financial requirements for pursuing new products/services, store locations, and the like. Explain how you will raise the needed capital. Include capital equipment, buildings, inventory, advertising, and other pertinent information in your requirements list. Identify whether you will use debt or equity to raise the needed capital for future growth.

Personnel requirements

3. What management personnel and other employees will be needed to support the projected growth?

List additional management personnel and other employees needed to support future growth. List job titles, brief job descriptions, salary, and benefits.

Exit strategy

4. How will the growth plan enable the owner or investors to obtain an exit?

Explain in detail how the growth plan will enable the owner or investors to obtain an exit. Explain future plans for going public, merging with a public company, selling for cash, or other exit strategies. Provide an exit plan for your investors that shows how and when they will get their cash back on their investment. If the venture is a family business, explain how the business will be distributed to the siblings.

Business Plan Appendix

It is important that the business plan not be filled with a lot of detail that will not interest many readers. The appendix is the appropriate place to put all supporting documents for many of the forecasts made in the business plan. This is the catchall section that can turn out to be lengthy. In some business plans for high-tech products, the appendixes were made into separate documents because of their length. The appendix demonstrates that the entrepreneur has done a significant amount of thinking and planning in all areas of the venture and has documented his or her projections. These exhibits lend credibility to the plan and assist in obtaining funds for the venture. Ensure that these exhibits are attractive, readable, and understandable.

The appendix does not have section titles. Instead, include a title page for each section of exhibits. Include the following in the appendix:

- Historical balance sheet or start-up funding & expenditures, sales projections, inventory projections, operating expenses projections, capital budget projections, equity & debt worksheet, and amortization schedule, if applicable.
- Detailed resumes of the management team or key personnel who are or will be working in the venture. Highlight the qualifications that directly relate to the business concept.
- All employee contracts, stock option plans, retirement plans, and so forth. Include a copy of the detailed document.
- Personal financial statements for each of the principals. Use standard bank form.
- Copies of patents, copyright approvals, or other applications along with detailed documentation.

- Actual documents of agreements: partnerships, sales, distributor contracts, noncompete/nondisclosure, corporate bylaws, and other legal documents.
- Samples of product and service brochures or other advertising.
- Copies of any logos developed.
- Copies of reference letters, recommendations, or endorsements. Don't use letters more than 12 to 16 months old.
- Copies of related market studies or articles from trade journals or other appropriate media. Include the source and date.
- Professional photographs of the product, facilities, or equipment. Place in plastic pages to protect pictures.
- Any detailed outlines of the operating/control systems. Include business or operating manuals.
- Any customer-signed orders or letters of intent. Use only current orders or letters not more than two years old.
- Any related information to support the industry study, such as demographics or magazine articles. Use clear copies and include the source and date.
- Detailed descriptions of products. Many readers want to know in detail how the product functions.
- A map showing the location of business.
- A copy of any credit reports on the business.
- The last three years of tax returns and any other historical financial statements.

Following these guidelines will enable entrepreneurs to write a compelling and professional business plan. Remember that "to fail to plan is to plan to fail." Following this process increases the chance of success. Good planning!